Ballooning Handbook

C-GSB

Ballooning Handbook

Don Cameron

Pelham Books

Evercreech 12 May 1985

First published in Great Britain by
Pelham Books Ltd
44 Bedford Square
London WC1
1980

British Library Cataloguing in Publication Data

Cameron, Don
Ballooning handbook.
1. Hot air balloons – Piloting
I. Title
629.132′522 TL638

ISBN 0 7207 1220 3

Set, printed and bound in Great Britain by
Fakenham Press Limited, Fakenham, Norfolk

Contents

Acknowledgements 6
Preface 7

1 **Fundamentals of Ballooning** 9
History of Ballooning 9
A First Balloon Flight 9
Lighter than Air 12
The Modern Hot-Air Balloon 14
Controls and Instruments 16

2 **Flying Techniques** 22
Choice of Take-off Site 22
Laying Out and Inspection 23
Briefing of Ground Crew 25
Inflation 25
Pre-Take-off Checks and Passenger Briefing 27
Take-off 29
Control in Flight 30
Fuel Management 34
Gusts and Crosswinds 35
Flight in Thermal Conditions 35
Pre-Landing Checks and Passenger Briefing 36
Landing 36
After Landing 39
Emergency Procedures 39

3 **Advanced Flying Techniques** 42
Altitude Flying 42
Distance and Duration Flying 47
Record Breaking Formalities 51
Night Flying 52
Flying over Water 55
Mountain Flying 56
Competition Ballooning 61
Commercial Ballooning 62
Launching Hang Gliders 64

4 **Hot-Air Balloon Technology** 67
Envelopes 67
Burners and Fuel Systems 75
Tank Valves and Hose Connections 79
Baskets and Suspensions 88
Instruments 90

5 **Navigation** 93
Measures of Distance 93
Measure of Direction 94
Maps and Charts 95
Balloon Navigation 99

6 **Meteorology** 102
Atmosphere 102
Clouds 103
Depressions and Fronts 105
Temperature Lapse Rates 106
Convection 108
Wind-induced Turbulence 111
Lee Waves 114
Anabatic and Katabatic Flows 116
Sea Breezes 116
Radiation Fog 117
Surface and Upper Winds 118
Effect of Rising Ground 118
Altimeter Setting Procedures 118

7 Ballooning Law 122
Air Navigation Order 1976,
Article 7 122
Article 39 123
Article 65 123
Air Navigation Order 1976,
Schedule 1 124
Schedule 9 126
The Rules of the Air and Air Traffic Control Regulations 1976,
Section II 127
Section III 130
Section IV 132
The Civil Aviation (Aerial Advertising) Regulations 1971 132
Notams and Aeronautical Information Circulars 133
The Legal use of VHF Radio in Balloons 135
Will there be a Clampdown on Ballooning? 136

8 Organization for Ballooning 140
Ownership 140
Transport 142
Fuel Supplies 142
Training 144
Maintenance 145
Logbook Entries 148
Certificate of Airworthiness 149
Inspection Schedule 149
Insurance 151
Income and Sponsorship 153

Appendices 155
1 Requirements for Pilots' Licences (UK) 155
2 Notes on Required Pass Standard for Balloon PPL Flight Test 156
3 Syllabus for Written Examinations and Flight Exercises 158
4 Examination Papers 160
5 British Balloon and Airship Club Code of Conduct 164
6 Weight Calculations 165
7 International Classes 168
8 World Records – Hot-Air Balloons 169
9 Bibliography 170
10 Useful Addresses 171

Index 173

ACKNOWLEDGEMENTS

The extracts on pages 18 and 40 are from *Lighter than Air* by Stephen Wilkinson. The stories on pages 32 and 60 are by kind permission of *National Geographic Magazine* and John Gore respectively.

Appendices 2–7 inclusive appear by courtesy of the Civil Aviation Authority.

The maps and map symbols are reproduced by kind permission of Ordnance Survey and the Civil Aviation Authority.

The cloud photographs are reproduced by courtesy of the Royal Meteorological Society. Other photographs are by Tom Sage (*pages 17 and 74*), Clive Landen (*page 53*) and the author. All the line drawings are by Tony Mould.

Preface

Modern hot-air ballooning is a relatively new branch of sporting flying. It has been going in Europe for only twelve years, and in the USA for about six years before that. Its real growth has only taken place in the last three years or so.

I have often been asked to recommend books covering the studies required for the Private Pilot's Licence (Hot-Air Balloons) and have never been able to give a satisfactory answer. Some books cover parts of the field admirably, but there is no book which is written for the balloon pilot. That is my reason for producing this volume.

The material covered is that required for the PPL (mainly Chapters 1, 2, 5 and 6), and a little beyond. The aim is to help pass the examinations, but also to whet the appetite to move on to greater things.

Experienced pilots often say that there is more to flying training than time in the air and book learning. By being around, hearing current news and views and hearing of the misfortunes and close shaves of others a fabric of experience is gradually woven. The flying club bar is, in fact, a great seat of learning. I have included a few of these 'bar stories' throughout the volume and I hope that they will instruct and entertain. Taken one after another they form a series of horror stories and I hope that the reader who has not yet ventured aloft by lighter-than-air craft will not be put off. It is important to recognize and stress dangers, but we can also console ourselves with the thought that ballooning has one of the safest records of all air sports. Balloons are simple with few things to go wrong, and speeds are low.

I have tried to write this book in international terms, but units of measurement, air laws and ballooning customs vary throughout the world. The units used are the old-fashioned American/British, with metric equivalents noted in parentheses where appropriate. Altitudes are always in feet as this is the international air traffic control standard and temperatures are in Celsius throughout.

Don Cameron
June 1980

Anthony Smith, one of the founders of the British Balloon and Airship Club, taking off with a passenger in a gas balloon.

1 Fundamentals of Ballooning

History of Ballooning

On 21 November 1783, man first took to the air. The aircraft was a hot-air balloon, but very different from today's sporting craft. Pilatre de Rozier and the Marquis D'Arlandes kept themselves up over Paris for twenty-five minutes by energetically stoking their brazier with straw and twigs to keep the balloon hot. Even a modern hot-air balloon requires constant reheating, and a balloonist today can smile at the account of the conversation in the balloon. The Marquis had been admiring the view of the river and Pilatre de Rozier urged him to stoke faster with the words: 'If you look at the river in that fashion you will be likely to bathe in it soon. Some fire, my dear friend, some fire!'

The hot-air balloon may have been the first aircraft, but the gas balloon was not far behind. On 1 December 1783 Professor Charles demonstrated the first hydrogen balloon in an equally successful ascent from Paris.

Charles' balloon was a much more practical device than the hot-air balloon of those days and differed very little from the majority of gas balloons flying today. For almost two centuries hot-air balloons were virtually ignored until the late 1950s when a balloon was built as part of a United States Government research programme. This balloon was of man-made fibres and was filled with air heated by a propane flame. The modern hot-air balloon was born.

Since that first balloon, which showed that a practical balloon with an operating cost of about one per cent of that of a gas balloon could be made, hot-air ballooning has expanded all over the world. It has attracted thousands of adherents and is still one of the fastest growing air sports.

A First Balloon Flight

Everyone has a different reaction to his or her first balloon flight: a mixture of fear, appreciation of beauty and wonder that the thing works at all.

The first thought is certainly apprehension. The balloon arrives on a small trailer. The basket seems so small for two people, that it is surprising when the pilot explains that this one is actually for four. It contains a lot of technical-looking gear – fuel tanks strapped in the corners and a burner unit which seems to be mostly coiled tubing. The balloon itself is reputed to be inside a rather scruffy canvas bag which lies behind the basket on the trailer. It is difficult to imagine that this is a safe flying machine.

The pilot, and others who have an opinion, discuss at length whether the weather conditions are safe enough for a flight and finally decide that it is rather poor, but just good enough to go ahead. This reinforces the feeling of apprehension.

The balloon is unloaded from the trailer, with much heaving and puffing, and the basket is laid on its side with the burner in position. The envelope is attached and spread out on the grass. The fabric appears thin, about the consistency of a man's shirt instead of the expected canvas. Then the top parachute valve must be put in. A large circular section of the balloon envelope is not attached to it, but is held with little Velcro tabs at intervals, but it's all right according to the pilot, as it is held by air pressure in flight.

Now the pilot directs two crew members to hold the crown down and two others to hold the base of the balloon open. Some cold air is blown into the envelope either using a motor-driven fan or by flapping the envelope base.

The pilot then takes his position behind the burner, like the operator of a machine gun, and gives a blast of flame. It is about seven feet (two metres) long and is an impressive fiery monster. At this point the question uppermost in the mind of the first-time passenger is how to escape without losing face, but it is too late for that.

As the heat enters the envelope there is a magical transformation. The flat lifeless mass of fabric begins to breathe, rise up and expand. Somehow the beauty of this contradiction of the law of gravity makes all the complexity of a tangled technical contraption on the ground transform itself into a shape which seems so pure and natural that it should not be called a 'machine'. Looking up inside the balloon the regular and colourful space is like a vast piece of architecture – the inside of a giant cathedral dome.

The pilot works through his check list, calls for all passengers to board (much too late to back out now) and heats up. Slowly the balloon feels lighter and finally the basket slides a little over the ground and lifts off. There is no motion of any kind, rather the impression that the earth is leaving the balloon and the crowd of helpers at the launch point is sinking away below.

The balloon rises above the tree-tops and, after the first ascent, there is no feeling of height. All fear disappears and the main impression is the beauty and magic of the experience. It is quite unlike an aeroplane; there is no motion and no one has ever been travel sick in a balloon. There is also no wind because the balloon is travelling with the wind making the relative air movement zero. A ribbon hung from the basket of a balloon would hang straight down.

The balloon must be kept warm so in normal flight the pilot operates the burner for five seconds and then leaves it off giving silent flight for twenty seconds. A little more frequent burning causes the balloon to rise and a little less allows it to descend.

It is possible to fly low enough and slowly enough to hold conversations with people on the ground.

Great control is possible. The balloon may fly above the clouds where the stationary carpet of mist looks so near and so permanent that it would be possible to get out and walk on it (but it is not advisable to try!). Also visible on above-cloud flights is the balloon's shadow, which by a trick of light-interference shows a coloured halo around the basket. Low-level flight is easily controlled and again quite different from an aeroplane. It is possible to fly at very low altitude at only a walking pace (if the wind is slow enough). This gives enough time to have a conversation with people on the ground.

At the end of the flight the pilot selects a field free of crops or animals and touches down. In quiet conditions this will be light as a feather, just like the take-off, but when it is windy the basket may tip over and drag until the pilot has deflated the envelope by pulling the red line. When everything stops the passengers can then disentangle themselves and step out.

A skilful pilot will have guided his aerostat to a spot near a country pub so that, after packing the balloon and visiting the farmer, the flight can be celebrated in a suitable manner. By long tradition it is the duty of the first-time aeronaut to provide champagne!

Lighter than Air

In ordinary experience air appears to be extremely light, but this is a misconception. Imagine a cube of air measuring ten feet along each side. This volume, 1,000 cu. ft, contains at standard conditions about 76 lb of air (one cubic metre contains 1·25 kg of air).

A typical four-person balloon has a volume of 77,000 cu. ft (2,180 cu. m) and contains approximately 2·6 tons of air before heating.

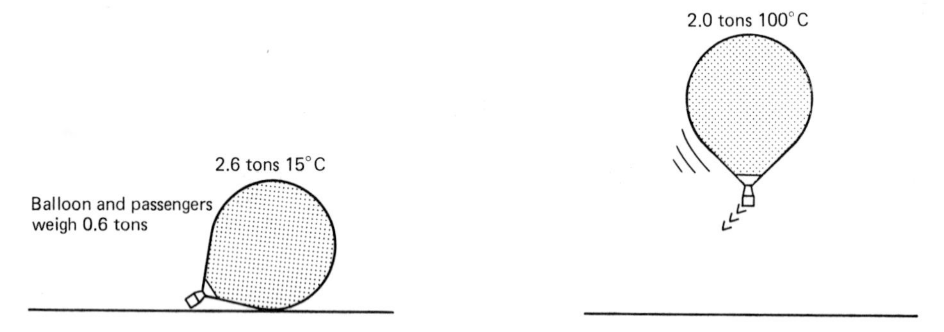

Fig. 1.1 Heating to achieve buoyancy.

When heated, the air expands and part of it is expelled through the mouth of the balloon. The balloon equipment and passengers generally weigh about 0·6 ton and so this is the amount which must be driven out before the balloon will be buoyant and ready to fly. It is achieved in this example at 100 °C – a typical flying temperature.

The lift of a hot-air balloon is only a small fraction of its total displacement and, for this reason, it must be made much larger than a gas balloon to give the same lift. For example, to give a lift of 0·6 ton, comparative volumes required are:

hot air	77,000 cu. ft (2,180 cu. m)
hydrogen	19,000 cu. ft (538 cu. m)
helium	20,500 cu. ft (580 cu. m)

Gas balloons can be made much smaller and this is an advantage, but even so their use is ruled out for most balloonists on grounds of cost.

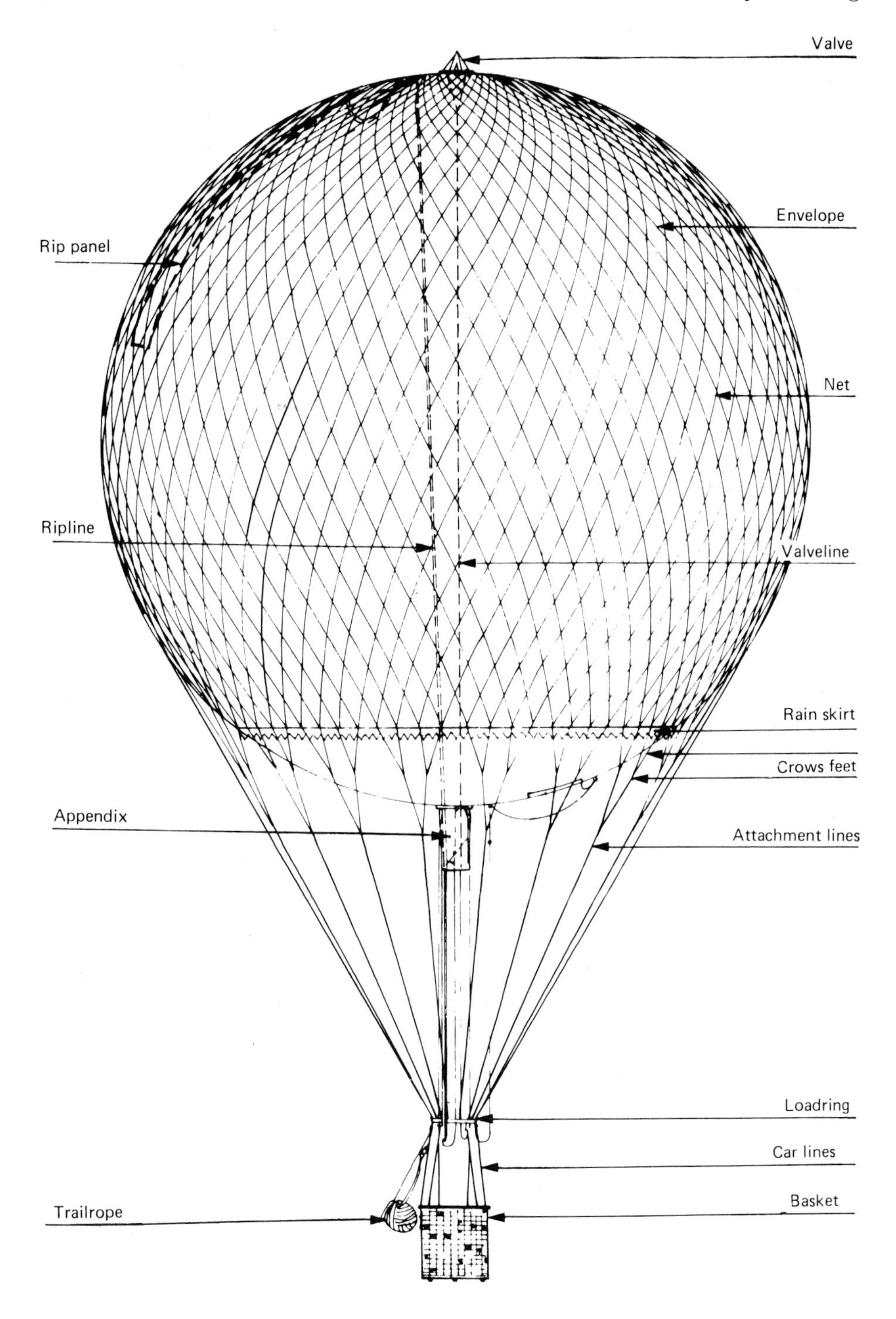

Fig. 1.2 Gas balloon.

The Modern Hot-Air Balloon

Since their beginning, modern hot-air balloons have undergone rapid development, although the basic features have remained unchanged and are common to all makes.

The envelope is constructed of nylon or polyester fabrics and is reinforced with strong webbing tapes. The main flight loads are carried by the envelope and a supporting net of the gas balloon type is not used. Steel wire cables at the base of the balloon support the basket or gondola.

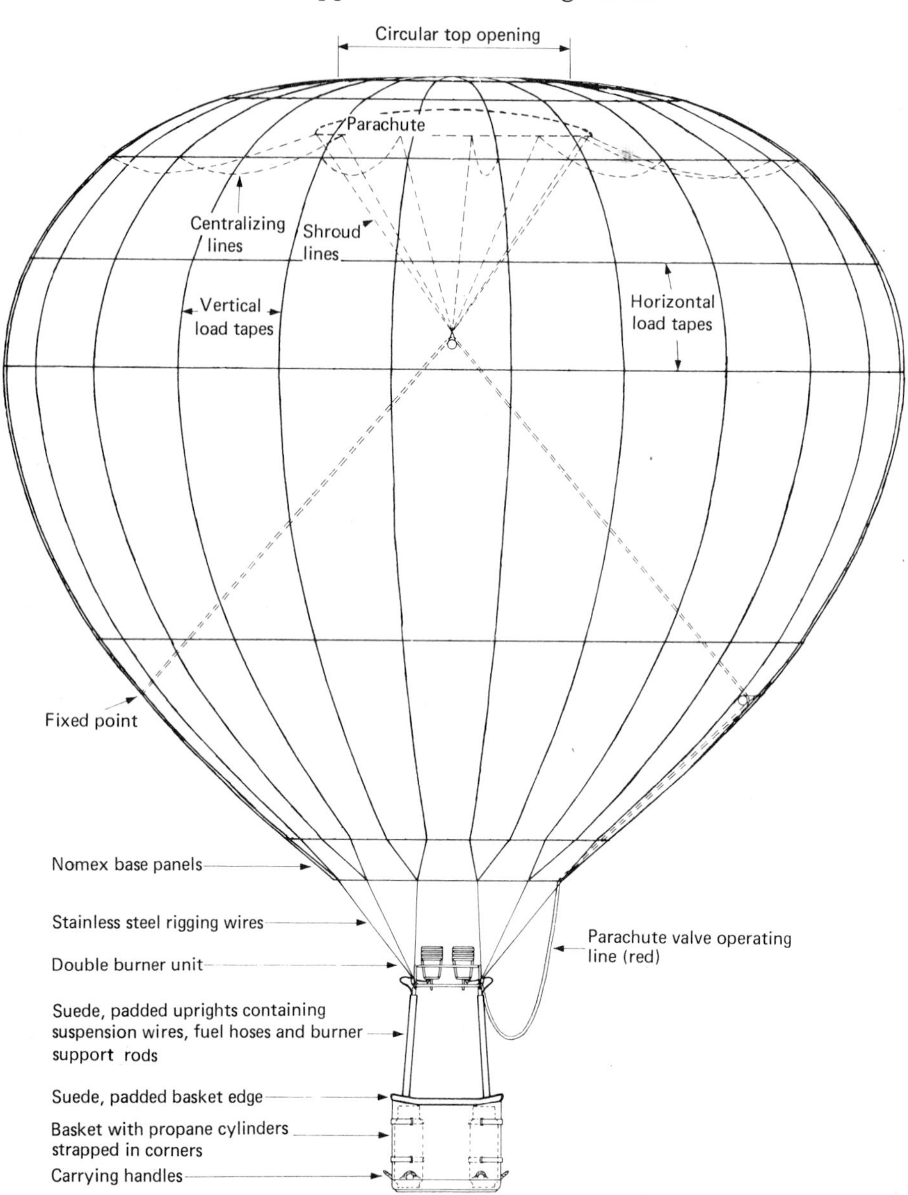

Fig. 1.3 Hot-air balloon.

The air in the balloon is heated and kept hot by a propane burner which draws its fuel in liquid form from cylinders in the basket and vaporizes it in a coiled tube in the flame.

A balloon is one of the simplest forms of aircraft and this gives a potential for safety and reliability which can be realized with safe and informed piloting.

The balloon and basket with a fan for initial inflation.

Controls and Instruments

The controls are also simple:

Blast valve: The burner is usually controlled with a valve which is either full on or full off. This gives the most sensitive control and avoids the freezing problems which a throttling valve would cause. In normal flight the burner is turned on for five seconds or so and off for twenty seconds. By varying the timing of the burner the pilot can control climb or descent and, with practice, can control the flight path with great accuracy.

Rip line: The rip line pulls a panel out of the top of the balloon causing rapid deflation. It is used to stop dragging on windy landings, and obviously can be used only on the ground or a short distance above it. The line is coloured red and is secured by thread safety-ties which must be broken before it can be operated.

Vent line: A vent which can be opened and reclosed in flight to allow a controlled release of hot air is often used. It is operated by a white line from the basket.

Parachute valve: A new feature which has become increasingly popular is a parachute valve. It is just like a parachute, with circular canopy and shroud lines and it plugs a circular opening in the top of the balloon. A line from the base of the shroud lines allows it to be pulled downwards to allow release of hot air and this system can be used in place of the rip panel and vent (see Figs. 1.2 and 2.1).

Trailrope: A heavy rope which can be thrown overboard when near to the ground to act as a frictional brake and a stabilizer. Owing to the large size of hot-air balloons compared to gas balloons, the trailrope is almost completely ineffective and is now used solely on gas balloons.

Handling line: A light line which can be thrown to the crew to guide the balloon clear of obstacles when becalmed.

Instruments: Few instruments are required for ballooning and it is quite usual to fly with no instruments at all. Instruments typically used are the altimeter, rate of climb meter, envelope temperature gauge, fuel tank gauges and burner pressure gauge.

Some countries such as the USA and Germany have made all these instruments a legal requirement.

A watch is also useful and at times the 'basic instruments' have been defined for examination purposes as an altimeter and a watch.

Instruments are often obscured by the instructor during the early stages of training as it is important to learn to fly using the visual impression of the balloon's flight path.

FACING PAGE: A hot-air balloon preparing to take off in the town square, St Niklaas, Belgium.

OO-SAX
Marlboro
VP

On October 30, 1918, I was 'detailed' as pilot for the 80,000-cu. ft balloon 'W' I, which was due to leave the polo ground at Hurlingham at 11.15 'ack emma'. Eight passengers were to accompany me, and the party included Brigadier-General F. E. McClean (now Sir Francis McClean, A.F.C.). There was a very strong wind blowing when we arrived at Hurlingham, and only two balloons were being filled on account of the ever-increasing velocity and unsatisfactory weather reports. Strange to relate, the wind was blowing almost due north, and I at once saw the possibility of making a record flight if we could get away early in the day. At 2,000 ft there was a wind well over 40 mph, and a much greater velocity at higher altitudes. A balloon has never flown from London to Scotland, and after my experiences I doubt if such a flight is possible. Unknown to my passengers, I decided to make the attempt to cross the border before we came to earth.

During the filling process the breeze freshened in an alarming manner, and the huge balloon was being held down with the utmost difficulty, and at times the envelope actually touched the ground when swaying in the wind. Notwithstanding the great number of ballast bags filled with tons of sand, the 'gas-bag' was continually making great leaps and bounds over the ground, rising at times to about twenty feet. To help the men in rigging and 'holding down' preparatory to flight, about 200 R.E. men were requisitioned and two more guyropes attached with releasing hooks to be operated on the word 'let go'.

During a lull in the proceedings I took over and told the 'crew' to get into the basket with me. Being mostly Officers from the Grand Fleet, no time was lost, which was more than fortunate, for before we could get properly weighed, a terrific wind swept the ground and the balloon became so violent in its antics that the R.E. men got 'breeze up' and let go the ropes. We whizzed over the ground, laden with superfluous ballast, and making straight for a large block of buildings; but there was no 'breeze up' among the sailors, for they worked like mad, throwing out bags to give us 'lift', and we cleared the buildings by about ten feet, but managed to take a flag-pole off with the basket as we passed by. The pole snapped off like a carrot and fell with a clatter on to the roof and then down into the street below. Luckily the appendix of the envelope had successfully opened, and for the time being all was well but we had lost a great deal of ballast and shot up to over 9,000 ft, and well above the layer of thick clouds and mist obscuring the earth below. I had now plenty of time to think out a plan of action, and in a short time the basket ceased to oscillate and we were at peace, and travelling along in silence at a terrific pace. In about twenty minutes' time I decided to come down through the clouds and find our bearings by map and compass. To my astonishment we were well away and some 60-odd miles north of London, and at times must have been travelling 70 to 80 mph, which promised well for the attack on Scotland.

There were, however, many conditions to be taken into consideration if a high altitude was to be maintained and speed continued, for the great weight of eight passengers in the balloon would soon cause us to descend, and the only way to keep height and speed was to drop a passenger. To do this at the speed we were travelling seemed an impossibility, but I determined to try it, and one of the 'Grand Fleet' was only too glad to make the attempt and, if possible, keep a 'date' he had in London that night.

Careful manipulation of the valve and a search for a sheltered spot in a valley was the next effort, and by taking the basket through a stiff hedge or tree the job might be managed. After much searching and fixing a gliding angle we found a suitable place, and I managed to take the basket through a stiff hedge and the sailor dropped off the edge in a field near Stamford in Lincolnshire. This was most beautifully done, and the jump was made at a height of about three feet during a slight stoppage after passing through the hedge. The 'Grand Fleet' rolled over on its back and, recovering waved a cheery farewell as we shot up to 6,000 ft as a result of this loss of 'ballast'.

Our altitude was now all that could be desired and there was a wind of great velocity, so we did not come down until well over the Humber past Hull and were making excellent progress, when the wind began to blow slightly from the west and I realized that to make Scotland was impossible. I tried all altitudes and every possible manœuvre to recover direction, and though I did at times succeed we had drifted gradually to the east coast, and if we were to continue our flight the final descent would be in the North Sea somewhere north of Whitby.

The wind above also began to decrease but the ground speed was well over 60 mph, and the possibility of being unable to land *anywhere* without serious consequences began to arise with alarming suddenness.

We had seen the other balloon 'land' at Cranwell aerodrome, and from the appearance of the landing they must have had a most unpleasant time, as we saw the basket crash into the wall of a small building, and after parachuting and dragging off half the roof, break away again and continue to drag the basket with its occupants for about a mile over the fields, and we were all devoutly thankful we were not in that balloon. The General Hospital at Lincoln received some members of the crew, one of whom had a badly fractured thigh. This landing acted as a warning to me, and I had no idea of landing anywhere but a sheltered valley if possible. For many miles I tried in vain to find such a place, but our speed was too great to attempt to land and there always seemed to be some obstacle ahead in direct line of flight in the form of farm buildings or other equally uninviting full stop. We continued our mad and helpless flight until well north of Scarborough, when the situation began to become desperate, and there was nothing for it but to land anywhere and anyhow. Failing a speedy landing we were 'for it' in the North Sea, and unless speedily rescued by some passing boat, should all be drowned and 'Balloons, One' struck off the active list, and the daily 'Wastage of Pilots' increased by yet another 'Balloonatic' and the loss of a Brass Hat in the shape of a Brigadier-General would also have to be added to the day's bag.

I prepared to land as soon as we were well clear of Scarborough, and let down the 300 feet of trailrope in the hope of it catching in some tree or obstacle and reduce our speed. Weather conditions began to assume that 'East Coast Complexion' of sea roque, drizzling rain and gloom, and with Whitby and the chill North Sea looming ahead, there was an ominous silence in the basket, the Navy

Flight of a military balloon (Royal Flying Corps). London to Bickley Moor, Yorkshire, 210 miles. Time in air, four hours, fifteen minutes. A sketch from memory of the landing, 30 October 1918.

living well up to its tradition in this respect. The huge gas-bag was flapping about above and breaking the silence in a dismal manner, and at 300 ft we had lost all our ballast and gradually descending at a terrific speed – falling like Lucifer, certainly in our case – never to rise again. The trailrope was whistling over the fields and hedges with occasional jerks and tightenings as it momentarily caught in gates and hedges. We were now whizzing over the heather-covered Yorkshire moors,and the prospects of a tolerably safe landing became more possible, when there was a sudden stoppage which upset all my calculations. The basket shot out at right-angles, whilst the envelope filled with wind and tried to form a parachute in the top of the net, and a pile of bodies at the bottom of the basket was the result of the sudden stoppage. Being fairly accustomed to this kind of thing I was the first to 'break away' and look over the side to see what had happened.

I found that the trailrope had become securely lashed round the trunk of a large holly tree growing about six feet away from the edge of a deep stone quarry, and we were temporarily suspended about 500 feet above the earth below. Fortunately the rope had completely knotted itself round the tree (discovered afterwards) and fortunately held and did not break under the terrific strain. The parachuting envelope helped to add to the pull, and it was impossible for this state of affairs to last more than a few minutes. The tree began to slowly come away from the earth, and we plunged and yawed about in a most alarming manner – at times we went down to within fifty feet of the ground below, only to be shot up again to the extreme length of the rope, which threatened to wrench the tree out with its roots. It was during one of these upward rushes that the tree did actually come away, and at the same time bringing tons of stones and earth clattering down into the quarry below. We were loose and off again all the time rapidly descending, but this time with a glorious improvised anchor and drag in the form of the holly tree, which crashed and bumped into every obstacle in its path. We had clear country ahead now, so I threw out the grapnel and awaited results. We travelled for a few miles when a small gamekeeper's hut came into view and directly in our line of flight, and we made a glorious 'direct hit' broadside on to the hut. The effect was astonishing, there was a terrific crash and the air filled with broken bottles (empty whisky bottles they proved to be), and a small rusty iron stove made its first solo as an aeronaut, as the basket went clean through the hut. As we struck I pulled out the rip panel, and after about 100 yards of dragging we came to rest on the soft heather at Bickley Moor in North Yorkshire, having travelled 210 miles since we took off in London earlier in the day.

We had an adventurous landing, but there were no casualties, and having had our fill of aeronautics and aerobatics for the day, we left the balloon where it lay to be packed next morning. Friendly farmers came to the rescue and we spent a most festive night in a farmhouse, where we were shown what Yorkshire hospitality really meant. Next morning, after packing the balloon, we took it by road to the nearest station and left for King's Cross.

Lighter than Air
by Stephen Wilkinson

2 Flying Techniques

Anyone who can drive a car can learn to fly a balloon. It is an uncomplicated craft and its control in fair weather can be adequately mastered by any normal person in eight to twelve hours of instruction. But the learning process does not stop with the granting of a licence – rather it should be the beginning. The safest pilot is the one who works on building a fund of knowledge and practical experience throughout his flying career. Most ballooning mishaps are caused by pilot error rather than technical faults.

The greatest thing a pilot can learn is when not to fly. Some weather is not fit for any pilot to fly in, some only for pilots of a certain experience. The difficult thing is to judge one's own experience, and even this is something which must be learned. At times pressure from friends or commercial event organizers must be resisted, and – greatest of all the pressures – sometimes it is best to stay on the ground at a balloon meeting when others are taking off like a crowd of determined lemmings.

Choice of Take-off Site

The ideal take-off site is a grass surface sheltered by a tall bank of trees with a long unobstructed distance downwind. The ideal is not always available, however, and compromises have to be accepted. Balloons can successfully rise from show arenas, town streets, ships' decks and, in fact, almost anywhere. Each can be safe provided it is well thought out for the weather conditions of the day.

Shelter makes balloon inflation much easier and trees are ideal for this. For some aerodynamic reason solid obstructions are not quite so good. Buildings or solid pieces of ground seem to generate turbulence, whereas the 'feather edge' of a tree line allows a more gradual boundary between the sheltered air and the full wind speed above it. It is for similar reasons that the wind screens built years ago for airships were perforated.

When a scoop (see Chapter 4) is fitted the balloon can usually be inflated without shelter up to the maximum windspeed in which it is wise to fly, although it remains more relaxing to inflate in shelter if it is available.

The freedom from downwind obstructions must be considered in the light of the windspeed on the day. In still conditions a much steeper ascent can be

A sheltered take-off site.

relied upon. Very tall obstructions, such as towers or radio masts, can be dangerous even when quite a long way downwind; a collision is more severe at their height and the speed will be greater outside the surface layers.

Laying Out and Inspection

It is pointless to discover a fault in the balloon when at 500 ft and climbing. A good pre-flight inspection is a protection against any gross defects in the balloon, although we need not get to the point of doing a full C of A inspection before every flight. The balloon's flight manual will give a recommended list but the following is typical:

Basket wires undamaged and connected to burner.
Fuel tanks strapped in (contents checked) and burner hoses attached.
Check fuel system for any sign of physical damage, and check for leaks by admitting fuel to hoses and listening. Vent hoses afterwards.
Decide on load to be carried.
Envelope – check general condition, rigging to load frame, insert deflation panel (after laying out).

The basket is then placed on its side, burner facing downwind and the envelope wires are connected. Rigging is a simple job, although it is possible to put on the wires in the wrong order or get them crossed or twisted, so it is a job that has to be learned. While training it is a good idea to cast off the wires after each flight so that there is plenty of practice in rigging, even when circumstances allow the balloon to be loaded on to the trailer complete. There are two important 'don'ts' to be observed: don't leave karabiners on the envelope – it causes bigger tangles than it resolves, and don't decorate the balloon with extra numbers or colour codings to ease rigging. It is rather like typing with ten fingers, harder at first but faster after it is learned if you practise the right way from the beginning.

Once rigged, the balloon can be laid out in a long line downwind from the basket and spread out. It is important not to do this before it is really time to fly, as one of the factors causing fabric decay is sunlight. Do not use up your balloon's life on the ground.

Before flight the deflation system will require attention and this differs in the two main types.

Parachute tops are by far the easier of the two, and this is one reason for their growing popularity. Following the preceding flight the parachute must be pulled up from the deflation position well down the balloon, and small Velcro tabs pushed into position to hold the parachute in place during the early stages of inflation. Sometimes the tabs are numbered to assist identification, but if not, it is easy to reach inside the balloon and follow up a parachute centralizing line to find the first tab position, and to follow round from there (Fig. 2.1).

Velcro tops require much more work. The ends of each straight section should be positioned together and the two end points pulled in opposing

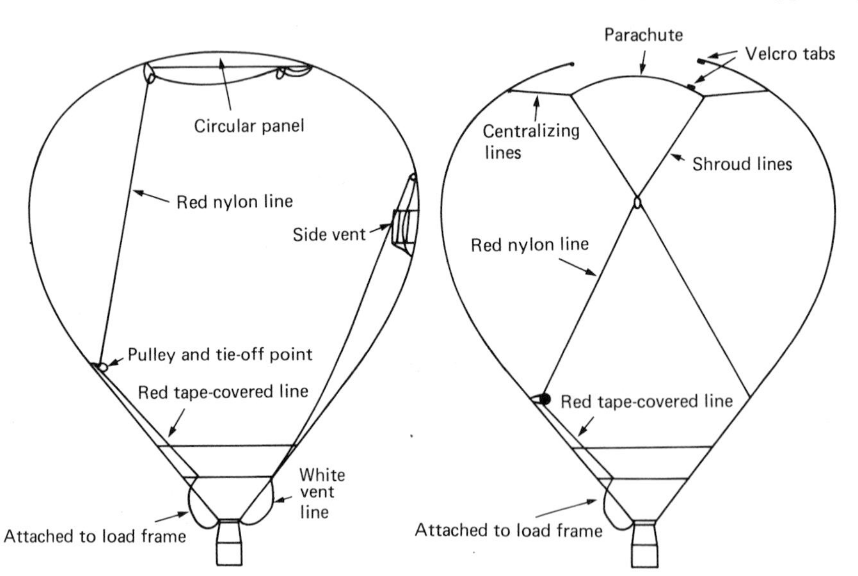

Fig. 2.1 *Left:* Velcro top balloon. *Right:* Parachute top balloon.

directions to tension the Velcro. A third person then positions the Velcro together and presses down firmly. This is repeated all round the panel until it is completely closed.

The next step is the rip locks (see illustration page 74). These must be made up and tied off by opening a small section of the Velcro. An important tip: Do not open the Velcro *at* the rip lock but to one side near it so that it is possible to lay the whole rip lock flat on the ground properly made up. If the Velcro is undone at the lock itself it is much harder to visualize its correct alignment and mistakes are easier. Some pilots get round this problem by going inside the balloon and checking all the cords at the same time, but this is not a good method. Pilots who believe in all this plodding around in the balloon can be recognized in the air by the accumulation of dirty footprints which decorate their aerostats.

On Velcro top balloons there is usually a side vent, but this requires no checking except to make sure that its line is present at the base of the balloon.

If a scoop is fitted it should be folded back under the mouth of the balloon at this stage. Do not attach it to the burner frame.

Briefing of Ground Crew

A proper briefing is important when working with inexperienced crew, and should include the following:

Crown line crew: not more than two people; do not wrap the line around the body or allow it to slip through the hands; wear gloves; refuse offers of help with determination; never be lifted off the ground.
Envelope mouth crew: wear gloves; stand outside wires; concentrate on holding the mouth high and the wires clear of the frame; do not pull the balloon back towards the basket; do not pull rip line.
Remaining crew: stand by basket, ready to restrain it against dragging or lifting; the envelope should not be handled during inflation except within six feet (two metres) of the mouth.

Inflation

After the slow work of preparation the inflation is exhilarating. The satisfaction of safely controlling a large and dangerous-looking flame, and breathing life into a flying monster many times larger than oneself never palls, even after hundreds of repetitions.

The inflation begins by introducing a little cold air into the balloon by 'flapping' the mouth, or by using a fan. Where a fan is available the balloon can be filled right up before turning on the burner and this makes it much easier to avoid burn damage. If there is no fan, the mouth crew end their flapping with an 'up-down-up and hold' and as this wavelike movement of the fabric holds the mouth momentarily wider open the pilot gives a carefully-timed puff of flame. If this is done well, a bubble is established which holds the mouth open for further heating. (It used to be common practice to send a volunteer inside the envelope to hold up the fabric, sometimes with a padded

Ready for inflation.

Inflation.

pole or broomstick. The unfortunate individual was known as 'Cremation Charlie', and his briefing included advice to get down low if the heat became oppressive, an agreed signal to stop burning and a caution not to walk too far up inside the balloon in case the crown was suddenly released.)

As the balloon inflates, the mouth crew will move from holding up the top of the mouth to holding the sides out and finally to holding the bottom down. The crown crew will slowly allow the crown to rise, until they finally walk in with the crown line to the load frame.

Burn damage used to be an accepted hazard in hot-air balloons and it was normal to fly balloons with ugly holes around the base. Flight manuals even specify maximum permissible damage at take-off. This is, typically: damage to fabric only, not load tapes, in the lower part of the envelope below the first horizontal load tape, provided it is of limited extent.

Nowadays, Nomex base panels and better piloting techniques have all but eliminated burn damage. Nomex is a fire-resistant fabric (which will char if determinedly roasted) and it is used for the base panels of most balloons.

The person behind the burner can do a lot to avoid burn damage. The first and most important caution is slow down! It is hardly ever necessary to hurry, so if fabric is getting near the flame or the mouth holder has allowed a rigging wire to dangle in front of the flame, simply do not burn, and ignore all excitement until it is clear again. Burn damage can also be avoided by using very short puffs of flame rather than a continuous blast.

As the balloon lifts into the vertical position the envelope mouth crew should take the scoop base to the burner load frame so that it can be clipped on, and the crown line should be brought in and attached.

The crew then position themselves on the basket to prevent dragging, to be ready to hold down on the pilot's command and to hold the scoop opening in the direction of the wind.

Pre-Take-off Checks and Passenger Briefing

In all forms of flying check lists are a tradition, and are a good way of making sure that nothing is forgotten at times when there may be considerable excitement. They should be learnt and used on every flight so that they become habit. Aeroplane instructors have devised many clever mnemonics for check lists and some have also been done for balloons, but I have always found it practical to remember checks starting at the crown of the balloon and working downwards. A sample check list is:

Envelope: General condition – free of damage, other than permitted base damage; tapes appearing correct without sign of undue strain; rigging wires correctly connected; karabiners closed.

Ripping panel – appearing correctly closed, line clear of rip lock hook slots, tie-offs unbroken; line attached to correct point on load frame. Valve – test working; line attached to load frame.

Parachute – test operation, line attached to load frame.

Pilot Burner: Running satisfactorily; normal appearance and sound; no freezing at regulator.
Burner Test: Note pressure from cylinder in use. It will vary from about 40 psi in winter to 150 psi in summer. Test also the second cylinder to be used and the other blast valve. It is not necessary to test cylinders beyond the first two, unless it is intended to fly over very difficult terrain where one cylinder would not be an adequate landing reserve.
Fuel: Have contents been checked? Memorize cylinder in use; check all others off.
Equipment: Matches, maps, instruments (if used), trailrope (if used) correctly stowed and attached to load frame.
Loading: Passengers aboard; have weight calculations been made?

The passenger briefing should include the following points: wear helmet (if used), wear gloves (if used), do not touch controls unless invited, do not hold on to fuel pipes, position of internal handles, do not leave basket on landing before receiving pilot's permission.

A newly qualified pilot returned home after completing his training for the licence several hundreds of miles away. His first flight on his own was to be at a local fair where, apart from one girl member of his team (called Sylvie Allione), no one had even seen a balloon before.

A large team of enthusiastic helpers were available, however, and unseen by the pilot fourteen willing people gathered on the crown line. The pilot heated and heated, until they eventually released the line. The balloon swept up, snatched the basket from the hands of the crew (except the girl) and climbed rapidly upwards. Sylvie was carried up holding onto the basket edge with her hands, and although the pilot and a crew member were on board their thick gloves prevented them from effectively holding her and pulling her on board.

At 200 feet altitude she fell, and was killed on impact.

This was Europe's first fatal accident in a modern hot-air balloon and like most air accidents it had several causes:

1 The pilot's lack of experience prevented him from recognizing that he had built up a very high lift.
2 The old-style crown line was relatively short, and had to be released when the crown crew was still out of sight of the pilot. The balloon would then rise with a swoop which, even on normal inflations, required restraint on the basket. Modern crown lines reach the ground even when the balloon is completely upright, and avoid this situation.
3 Crown crews on normal-sized balloons are briefed to *refuse help* and are limited to two or three since this accident.
4 When acting as ground crew there is a fixed rule to let go at once if your feet leave the ground. This must be automatic, as it will be too high to let go if there is the slightest hesitation. There is no need to worry about the pilot, his position inside the basket is comparatively safe whatever happens.

Take-off

Take-off, like almost every other part of ballooning, varies with the weather conditions.

In perfectly calm conditions, the best style of take-off is without ground crew. The crew are asked to stand back and the balloon is heated gradually increasing lift until movement in the basket shows that the balloon is light. A little more heat and the balloon lifts off in perfect equilibrium. With this type of take-off the pilot has control over his flight path from the start, and it is more satisfyingly precise than a take-off with excess lift.

When a wind of say over eight knots is blowing, the take-off becomes a difficult affair. As the balloon rises out of the shelter and meets the air blowing at the full wind speed there is a tendency for the wind to deform the balloon, slightly deflating it and losing some lift. The flame may also be deflected, so losing heat and preventing the replacement of the lift. The result can be a dangerous descent of the balloon, now accelerated to wind speed, into the downwind obstacles.

This problem is compounded by a phenomenon known as false lift. Any rounded surface held in a fluid flow will cause a suction force which tries to draw it into the stream. This is the surprising aerodynamic effect which is the principle of the aeroplane wing, and it can be verified by a simple experiment. Hold a spoon near a running tap as shown in Fig. 2.2. Instead of being deflected away by the flow it is firmly sucked in.

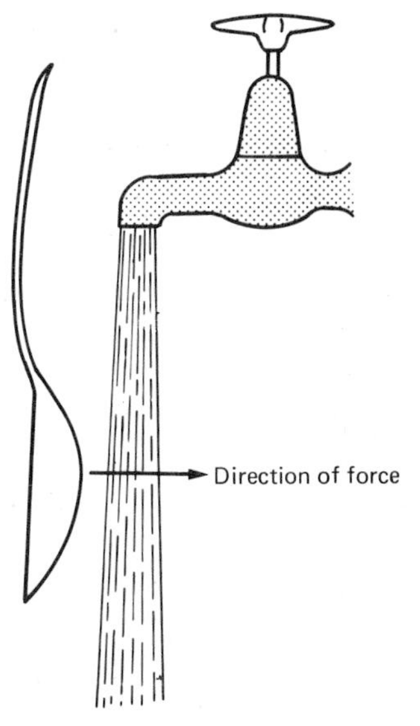

Fig. 2.2 The effect of flow over a curved surface.

The top of the balloon as it rises above the shelter is just like the curved back of the spoon, and the airflow over it creates a substantial lift. Unfortunately this lift is very temporary. It takes only a few seconds for the balloons to reach the same speed as the wind, and as the *relative* airflow drops to zero so does the false lift.

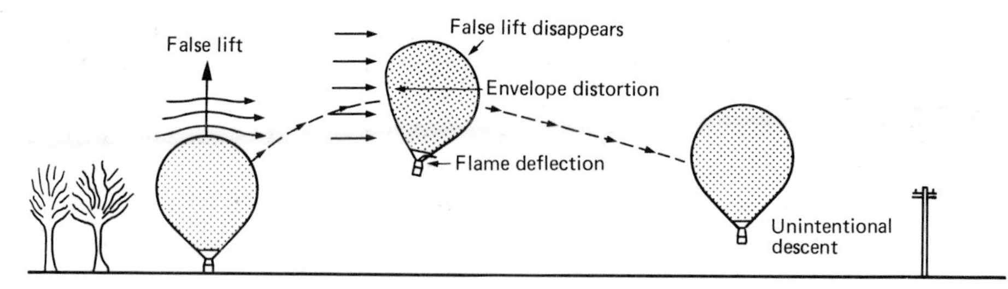

Fig. 2.3 The causes of unintentional descents during take-off from shelter.

Take-off from shelter should therefore be made with plenty of excess lift. Lift is built up on the ground with two or three helpers holding down the basket. The pilot calls 'hands off!' and the helpers let go momentarily. The motion, or lack of it, tells the pilot how much lift he has, and if it is not enough he calls 'hands on!' and continues heating. When the excess lift is enough a call of 'hands off and stand clear' is given and the balloon lifts away. Some pilots use a tether line equipped with a quick release to control excess lift on take-off.

The balloon should be heated to have enough excess lift on take-off but it is possible to have too much, putting an unreasonable strain on the balloon. Although most modern balloons will be strong enough to withstand any rate of climb which can be achieved without exceeding the maximum envelope temperature, it is bad practice to use a vastly greater excess than is necessary. The 'right' amount is something which must be learned during flying training.

The burner should be kept on while ascending until it is certain that the balloon will enter a steady climb and the pilot should give his full attention to the flight path of the balloon, leaving to his passengers the waving goodbye which is an essential part of a balloon departure.

If a scoop is fitted the balloon should be rotated by the ground crew before release so that its open side faces the wind which the balloon will meet as it climbs.

If no shelter is available, in windy conditions a take-off may sometimes be made by inflating the balloon as far as possible and then carrying the basket downwind to reduce the relative windspeed on the balloon. Only the pilot should be aboard at the beginning and the passengers should enter one by one as the lift builds up. Fortunately the 'running inflation', as this method is called, is seldom used nowadays as it is a cruelly exhausting task for the crew and generally leaves a trail of gasping bodies along the take-off run.

When a scoop is used, take-off without shelter is possible in almost all winds in which it would make sense to fly, without the necessity of a running inflation.

Control in Flight

Level flight is achieved in a balloon by intermittent use of the burner. This relationship between the burner and the time-lagged response of the balloon is the core of what is learned during flying training. Although it can never be learned from the pages of a book, it is useful to have a clear picture of the physical system which you are trying to control.

The balloon, as we know, contains an astonishing weight of air and when it is accelerated upward an equivalent weight of air must move downward to make room for it, and fill the space which it leaves behind. This movement of outside air means that the mass of air to be moved is effectively doubled.

Thus, when we accelerate a 77,000 cu. ft (2,180 cu. m) balloon whose displacement is 2·6 tons (as in our example on page 12), it will behave as if it had an inertia of 5·2 tons.

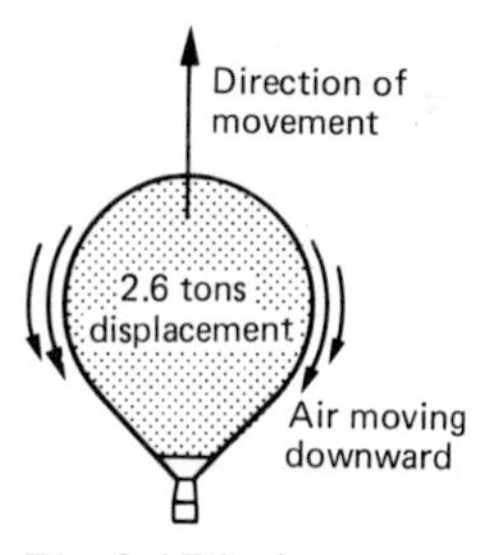

Fig. 2.4 Displacement of air and virtual mass.

The balloon flies in equilibrium at 100 °C internal temperature. Suppose it is heated to 110 °C to give an upward acceleration. This will take several seconds of burning to achieve and it will then only give an excess of lift of 117 lb (53 kg) to accelerate an effective 5·2 ton mass. Acceleration is not rapid with a hot-air balloon.

Despite this limitation, balloons can be controlled with great accuracy. It is simply a question of anticipating well in advance and of concentration. The timing of burns can be decided by watching the flight path and also by bearing in mind that the balloon is cooling all the time. If there has not been a burn for a longer than average time, it is probably time to put one in. Experienced pilots can keep the balloon well under control while talking to people on the ground, reading maps or doing many other things, but the student pilot should maintain one hundred per cent concentration on control of the flight path. There are some instructors who wait until there is ground below which is clear of dangerous obstructions then begin an interesting discussion with the student. If he forgets to burn long enough to be too late to avoid hitting the ground, it makes a good lesson in the need to concentrate.

After a few hours of practice surprising accuracy is possible. It is quite usual during low level practice for a student pilot to fly near enough to a tree-top to pick a leaf without any danger.

The characteristics of the balloon vary from winter to summer because of the variation in propane pressure. Typical values might be 40 psi (2·8 kg/cm^2) in winter to 150 psi (10·5 kg/cm^2) in summer. The balloon is much more difficult to control when the pressure is low, and it is best to fly with a lighter load than usual until experience is gained (see page 165).

Climbing is achieved simply by burning for relatively longer periods, although some limitations should be observed.

When flying at balloon meets where other balloons may be passing above, it is important to climb slowly. The rule is that the higher balloon, as he is the only one who can see, has the duty to avoid a collision by climbing but this may not be easy if the lower balloon is coming up fast. During the World Championships in 1977 in England one rapidly climbing balloonist looked up to find a basket shaped depression in the top of his envelope. The upper balloon managed to lift clear, but it was only by luck that no damage was done to the fabric or ripping panel closure of the lower balloon.

Keep burning and hope for the best....

Over the years one type of take-off accident has tended to repeat itself. The scenario is generally as follows:

The balloon lifts off in windy conditions without enough excess lift and skims low over the ground. The pilot burns and burns, but he is only countering the loss of false lift as the balloon gathers speed. As the balloon slides towards the downwind obstacles the more knowledgeable onlookers start to shout 'Rip! Rip!', but the pilot ignores them.

For some reason the natural reaction of a pilot with adrenalin surging through his veins is to keep burning long after it has become obvious that he has no hope of clearing the obstacles. The result is a costly although usually not dangerous crash into the trees, or whatever is in the way.

The moral of course is if in doubt, don't. When taking off in a higher wind speed towards obstacles you must be absolutely sure that you are going to clear them. If in *any doubt at all* rip out on the field ahead while there is still plenty of time. It means a little more work for the crew to drag it back and re-inflate, but this is nothing compared to a long and expensive repair. It certainly does not mean loss of face, for balloonists respect a decision which errs on the side of safety.

My burners roar their frenzied song. The altimeter needle winds swiftly around its dial. I recheck the ground handling lines dangling below and shudder, recalling a harrowing ascent two years ago: I had fancied I heard a muffled shout over the roar of the burners as I climbed swiftly past 300 ft. I shrugged it off, intent on watching the rate-of-climb indicator.

Later, as I cut back the burners at 3,000 ft, I heard someone call again – this time unmistakably.

'Please, mister, won't you get me down?' a child's voice whimpered desperately.

I looked overboard. The memory of what I saw still gives me nightmares. Somehow a boy had gotten a line wrapped tightly around his hand, and I had unwittingly lifted him with me!

I couldn't reach him, for the ground lines dangle straight down from the sides of the balloon, far from the gondola. As quickly as I could, I brought the balloon down, talking to the boy quietly, telling him to look at me, not at the ground.

Finally, two miles from our take-off point, 11-year-old Danny Nowell of Mill Valley, California, hit the earth – a little hard, and terribly frightened, but miraculously unscathed. Ever since, I have checked my ground lines with extra care.*

William R. Berry,
National Geographic Magazine, March 1966

* This incident would be unlikely to happen nowadays. No balloon is made now with handling lines from the sides of the envelope, and modern burners are so powerful that it would be impossible to keep burning constantly from the surface up to 3,000 ft.

Keep burning and hope for the best – stage 1.

Keep burning and hope for the best – stage 2.

Rapid climbs should also be avoided when an envelope thermometer is not in use as it is possible to overheat the envelope and balloons with Velcro ripping panels without rip locks should also be kept to a moderate rate of climb.

To descend the burner is left off for relatively longer periods. When descending from high altitudes it is possible to leave the burner off completely for a long time so that the envelope cools right down. The balloon should enter a stable descent at around parachute speed and this is known as a 'cold descent'.

The actual speed will depend on the design of the balloon, its loading and the temperature lapse rate of the atmosphere (see Chapter 6). During the descent some swinging, rotation, and envelope distortion may occur, but this should not be a cause for concern, provided it is not excessive.

Some balloons perform less well in cold descent, depending on the envelope shape; taller and narrower shapes seem to suffer more envelope distortion than average. Before attempting this manœuvre it is best to take advice on the behaviour of the balloon in use. When a scoop is fitted, it should be removed before attempting a cold descent, or if this is not possible it can be disconnected from the load frame and allowed to ride up.

Recovery from a cold descent should be initiated with plenty of height in hand (say 2,000 ft) and should be done with a series of short burns rather than a single long one. If the burner were turned on in cold descent and left on until descent stopped, there would be a vast excess of lift which would send the balloon shooting up again almost as fast as it had come down, and the envelope would probably become overheated.

The side vent and the parachute are a means of losing lift at a faster rate than normal cooling. During training it is best to try to do without venting altogether so that a good feel can be developed for the simple burning and cooling characteristics of the balloon. Most pilots use the vent very little in flight as it increases fuel consumption. It is used mostly in competition flying when rapid changes of direction are required.

The parachute is a very powerful method of reducing lift and care must be taken not to overdo it. When using parachute opening extensively in flight, always watch the envelope to observe the amount of deflation occurring. Under very light-loaded conditions some designs of parachute do not reclose automatically, but will do so if the burner is operated – this also requires a visual check.

Fuel Management

After the all-important task of controlling the flight path by means of the burner has been mastered, the pilot must also concentrate on fuel management. It is vital to be conscious of how much fuel is in each cylinder in the basket, which one is turned on and the sequence in which the others will be used.

The exact technique will depend on the fuel system layout of the balloon to be used and will be covered in detail in the flight manual. However, the following points are common to most balloons.

Only one tank should be open at a time (except when using a double burner). This keeps as much fuel as possible safely isolated and leaves only one valve to turn off in an emergency. Also, by emptying one tank at a time from start to finish it is easier to keep a mental picture of the amount of fuel remaining. Propane float gauges are very imprecise, and some balloons do not even use them, but it is perfectly safe to keep track of fuel contents by using isolated tanks in sequence.

When a tank runs out the propane liquid drops below the bottom of the dip tube and vapour is fed to the burner. Pressure falls rapidly, and this can be detected by the reduced size and noise of the flame and the reading on the pressure gauge. A vapour flame does not give a useful heat in ballooning terms, and several accidents and near-accidents have been caused by inexperienced pilots struggling to pull out of a descent unaware that their fuel tank has run out.

On balloons fitted with a vapour-fed pilot burner, one tank is fitted with a vapour valve and regulator to fuel the pilot. There is a difference of opinion as to whether this master tank should be used first or last in the sequence. If it is used last, the withdrawal of vapour throughout the flight will mean lower burner pressure when the liquid is used. If used first, care must be taken to leave enough fuel in the cylinder to maintain the vapour supply to the pilot. For a short flight this need not be a problem as the pool of propane left at the bottom of the tank after the liquid has fallen below the level of the dip tube is enough to run the pilot burner for an hour or so.

Gusts and Crosswinds

When a wind is felt in flight it means that the balloon has entered an airflow of a new speed or direction, and this relative airflow will act on the balloon until it has taken up the new velocity. Gusts tend to cause the balloon to lose lift by forcing some of the hot air out of the envelope, and also prevent its replacement by blowing away the heat of the flame. When a gust is felt it is best to start burning early, as an instinctive reaction, and to use the angle control on the burner to counteract the deflection of the flame by the wind.

Gusts and crosswinds are to be expected during thermic conditions, after take-off from shelter and near features such as hills, woods or buildings.

Flight in Thermal Conditions

Thermal conditions make control difficult, and they should be avoided by inexperienced pilots. Thermals produce strong horizontal gusts, and can also cause the balloon to climb, against the pilot's will, up to a few hundred feet. When caught in a thermal it is better to ride up with it, keeping the balloon hot until the altitude is greater than 500 ft. Otherwise there is a risk that the balloon, which has been allowed to cool, will leave the thermal and hit the ground before it can be reheated.

FACING PAGE:
A 500,000 cu. ft (14,156 cu. m) monster balloon, with a two-storey basket and room for over thirty people – the Gerard A. Heineken.

As the balloon continually changes horizontal direction in thermal conditions it becomes more difficult to plan a landing approach and great care is necessary.

If planning to take off in thermal conditions the best advice is 'don't'. However, if you must, fly lightly loaded, land with a large fuel reserve and concentrate very hard on making a safe landing. The balloon should have rip lock protection, a high-output burner and a skirt or scoop to shield the burner from turbulence.

Flight near cumulo-nimbus or thunderstorm clouds should be rigorously avoided. Such clouds often generate areas which are deceptively calm, but contain 'cells' of convection which produce vertical currents with speeds above 100 knots (50 m/s) and extend to many thousands of feet.

If a balloon were drawn into one of these rising currents there would be no means open to the pilot to leave it, and it is likely that turbulence sufficient to destroy the balloon would be found, or the balloon would be carried so high that the occupants would die from oxygen starvation or exposure.

Pre-Landing Checks and Passenger Briefing

Before settling down to make a landing approach, 'put the house in order' so that there will be no distractions during the critical approach phase. A typical set of pre-landing checks are as follows:

Envelope: Rip line available; valve line available.
Fuel: If fuel cylinder in use is nearly empty, switch to a fresh cylinder, if available.
Trailrope (if used): Attached to load frame rope ready for deployment.
Passengers: Briefed.
Equipment: Instruments, cameras, etc. made safe.

The passenger briefing is basically a repetition of the points made before take-off: wear helmets (if used), wear gloves (if used), touch controls only if asked (you may put one passenger in charge of the rip line), do not hold fuel hoses, hold on to internal handles and do not leave the basket without the pilot's permission (as the loss of one passenger's weight can cause an unintended take-off for those who remain).

Landing

Landing is the operation in balloon control which requires most judgement, and the flight test (see Appendix 2) consists, in practice, mainly of approaches and landings.

The type of landing which I favour is the low approach. The balloon is flown in a steady slow descent and is levelled off as low over the obstruction as safety permits. In stable conditions it will be possible to fly lower than in turbulent air.

The landing field will be chosen from what is available ahead, but, ideally, it should be a smooth grass field free of obstacles which might overturn the

Gerard A Hem

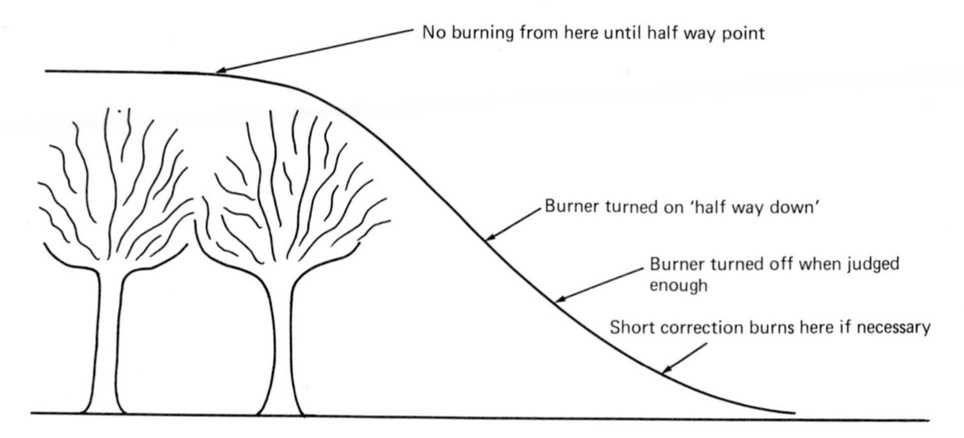

Fig. 2.5 Final landing approach.

basket and free of wires, livestock or crops. If possible it should be near a road.

As the chosen field is approached, the balloon is allowed to descend as it passes the last obstacle and burning is done on the 'half way down' rule. Half way down the burner is turned on, and turned off after sufficient burning. If the judgement is correct the balloon should round out at ground level with a zero vertical speed component.

After touchdown, or even slightly before, the rip panel or parachute is pulled out to its fullest extent and the balloon will deflate. If it is windy the basket will fall on its side and drag along and there is nothing the pilot can do except hold tight on the red line and wait for everything to stop. In these conditions it is wise to extinguish the pilot burner, and if time permits, turn off the fuel. In calmer conditions the balloon can be kept down using the vent or a slight parachute opening and passengers and fuel cylinders can be exchanged before taking off again.

It is impossible to learn how to land a balloon by reading about it, but I have found that this ideal procedure forms a good foundation on to which a student pilot can build his flight experience.

There are other approaches to landing. Some pilots favour the selection of a field at height and a steep direct approach into it. Fig. 2.6 shows the difference. My prejudice is that the high approach is likely to make a smooth controlled landing more difficult and make touchdowns in the correct part of the field (the upwind end) less probable. It is good to practise it a few times, however, as this method can be useful if it is ever necessary to come down quickly.

The landing itself should always be smooth no matter how bad the conditions – at least, that should be the aim. Occasionally in turbulent conditions it is necessary to land with a bump but it is very bad to become satisfied with frequent hard landings. They are not necessary and are the mark of poor piloting.

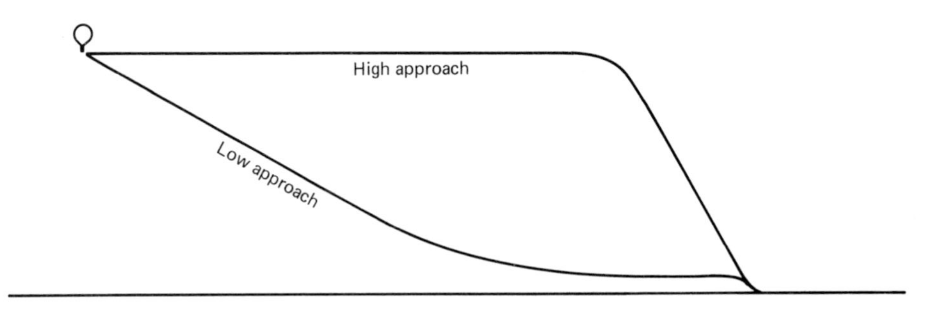

Fig. 2.6 Landing approaches.

After Landing

After landing the fuel lines should be emptied of propane and all valves checked off before packing up the balloon. The landowner should be consulted and his permission sought before bringing any vehicle on to the field. The code of conduct (see Appendix 5) should be scrupulously followed, because the future of our sport depends on maintaining a good reputation as responsible people with the farming community.

The flight should be entered in the balloon and pilot logbooks.

Emergency Procedures

Emergency procedures will normally be detailed in the flight manual for the make and model of balloon. These must be learned, and where appropriate practised during training. A typical list of emergency procedures is:

1 *Avoidance of dangerous obstacles at low level*

The pilot must decide whether to climb, or to make an emergency landing.

An emergency discharge of ballast can be effected by disconnecting the trailrope (if used) at the load frame, and dumping complete, or in extreme circumstances by dropping fuel cylinders.

Emergency landings can be made quite safely by opening the rip panel partially at heights of 50 feet or less.

2 *Preparation for a hard landing*

All passengers should be briefed to brace, watch the progress of the landing facing forward, and to hold on firmly to the basket's internal handles.

The pilot should shut the fuel off at the cylinder in use after the last burn, and if time permits empty the line, and extinguish the pilot light.

The pilot should have one hand on the burner, and should deflect it forward on landing away from the passengers and himself, unless a rigid superstructure is fitted.

Drop any available ballast e.g. trailrope. In extreme conditions the pilot may consider dropping fuel cylinders.

3 *Pilot flame failure*

If the pilot should go out for any reason, it should be relit if possible.

If this is not possible, the following procedure should be adopted: shut off main fuel at cylinder; open burner control valve fully; permit a small amount of fuel to enter the line by fractionally opening the cylinder valve; light main burner with a match or other igniter; open fuel cylinder fully to obtain normal burn; close cylinder down to a fractional setting to turn burner off but to maintain a pilot setting.

Do not use one cylinder as a pilot, with main fuel taken from another unless the pilot cylinder is giving vapour only. Prolonged restricted flow of liquid will cause freezing of the valves.

Make a landing as soon as possible.

4 *Fire on the ground*

Turn off fuel.

Put out fire with extinguisher.

If this is not attained within say 20 seconds ensure that all present retreat to a safe distance, as there is danger of explosion if the fire continues and causes rupture of the tanks.

5 *Fire in the air*

Turn off fuel.

Put out fire with extinguisher.

The pilot must identify the cause of the fire and decide if it is possible to relight the burner. If not the procedure for a hard landing above must be followed.

6 *Failure of a burner valve*

The feed pipes are long enough to reach the 'wrong' end of the basket so that all fuel cylinders could be used in the event of failure of one burner valve, although with zero reserve at the time of changeover. Land as soon as possible.

Things went badly from start to finish, and before the balloon was properly weighed and made ready, the weather conditions completely changed, and the wind tossed the balloon about the ground like a cork at sea, and it took the entire section of men we possessed to keep her steady and on the ground. As soon as a suitable lull came we cast off and let go, but at about ten feet a violent wind sent us crashing into the other balloon which was standing close by, and had been already filled. Our basket and 'gadgets' caught in the rigging and netting of the stationary balloon, and with the lift began to rip the net to pieces, so much so that the envelope nearly slipped out of the net. The most serious part of the 'beezness' was when one of the crew, in an effort to clear the basket, caught his arm in the netting, and had we not grabbed him, and held on he would have been pulled out of the basket. It looked as if his arm would be broken, and I was just about to rip the envelope and drop the balloon with a bump when scores of square yards of the netting gave way under the strain, and he became disentangled and we 'hauled him back again', and were able to laugh at what looked like being a most unpleasant accident. Once free, I poured out bags of ballast, which fell on to the 'Ack Emmas' below, and midst torrents of rain and blasphemy we shot up to 4,000 ft, where I found a wind of 35 mph in the direction SSW. The rainfall increased, and in no time the top of the balloon was full of water, and every time I pulled the valve a shower of filthy, gas-saturated water came down upon us in the basket. Clouds were very low, and it was difficult to find out where we were, but I continued the flight for about two hours, and as we were running short of gas, prepared to land. The envelope was now very empty and flopping about in the net, and we had little or no ballast left; it was very difficult to keep a height of even 500 ft. I had let down the trailrope, and we soon heard and felt it catching merrily on all kinds of obstacles below, but the blackness made it impossible to see anything that was happening. We were evidently passing over a village when the rope suddenly became firmly fixed on to some kind of spire or tower of a lofty building, and we were brought up with the usual jerk and held 'kiting' in mid-air, where we hung for about five minutes, and I was about to cut the rope when the wind increased the pull of the balloon, and there was a sensation of sudden release followed by the crashing of falling masonry below, and we were off again but descending with alarming speed all the time. The noise we made on being released must have disturbed the inhabitants, who probably thought there was an air-raid or something of the kind in progress, for the few lights were immediately extinguished, and there was a terrific blowing of policemen's whistles, and in the dark the form of a fire engine could be seen rushing up the main street to the scene of the crash. Wet through, with no ballast left, and only about a quarter of the balloon full of gas, we were certainly in for a rough landing; and with only a few minutes in which to get everything ready for the bump. We continued to fall at a most unhealthy rate, and in a good 35-mph wind when a dark patch of trees suddenly loomed out of the darkness, and as we went through them I ripped the panel out for its full length and awaited results. We landed as lightly as a feather in a large field immediately behind the trees, and without a breath of wind, owing to the excellent shelter and the fact that there was practically no wind at ground level. It was a miserable night,and we were miles from anywhere, and could not find a living soul anywhere around; but after searching I came across a deserted pig-sty, where we froze in a feeble attempt to sleep for the rest of the night. In the morning, I found we were somewhere on the edge of Salisbury Plain, with the nearest village some five miles away and no possible means of sending the regulation telegram saying we had landed safely; and on this occasion there was much anxiety as to our whereabouts, which was not allayed until late in the morning.

Lighter than Air
by Stephen Wilkinson
(A flight during the 1914–18 war in a gas balloon)

3 Advanced Flying Techniques

Modern hot-air ballooning is one of the newest ways to fly although it has the oldest history. Advanced techniques are being rapidly developed and records frequently broken. One of the things which makes it such an exciting sport is that it is still possible to discover new things.

Altitude Flying

Hot-air balloons are capable of flying to great heights, and generally do better in this environment than their occupants. Up to 10,000 ft no special precautions are necessary, and it is good to make one flight to this height during flying training. There is nothing difficult or skilful about it, but as almost all training balloon flights are made under 2,000 ft it widens the student's experience.

Flights above 10,000 ft present problems which become more severe the higher the planned flight. Some of the essential precautions are as follows:

Balloon lift and loading

A balloon heated to 100 °C will lose lift as altitude increases because of falling air pressure and density. The reduction in temperature with height reduces this loss of lift only slightly, but it is a help, and it is best to attempt high flights when the temperature aloft is low.

The formula for the lift of a hot-air balloon is:

$$L = \left[\frac{d_o T_o}{p_o}\right] V p_a \left[\frac{1}{T_a} - \frac{1}{T_b}\right] \text{ lb}$$

Where: d_o = surface density (lb/cu. ft), T_o = surface temperature (°K), p_o = surface pressure (lb/sq. ft), V = balloon volume (cu. ft), p_a = ambient pressure (lb/sq. ft), T_a = ambient temperature (°K), T_b = balloon temperature (°K).

Although the properties of the atmosphere vary from day to day, there is a conventional international standard atmosphere (ISA) which is a good starting point for our calculations:

INTERNATIONAL STANDARD ATMOSPHERE

Altitude (ft)	*Pressure* (lb/sq. ft)	*Temperature* (°C)
Sea level	2,116·2	15
5,000	1,760·8	5·1
10,000	1,455·4	− 4·8
15,000	1,194·3	− 14·7
20,000	972·6	− 24·6
25,000	785·3	− 34·5
30,000	628·5	− 44·4
35,000	498·0	− 54·3
40,000	391·8	− 55·3
45,000	308·0	− 55·3
50,000	242·2	− 55·3
55,000	191·0	− 55·3
60,000	150·9	− 55·3

Sea level density = 0·07657 lb/cu. ft
Temperature °K = 273 + temperature °C

Using standard sea level base conditions our formula reduces to:

$$T_b = 1/\left[\frac{1}{T_a} - \frac{95{\cdot}963L}{Vp_a}\right] °K$$

Let us work out two cases: A 77,000 cu. ft (2,180 cu. m) balloon flown solo weighing 764 lb (347 kg) and the same balloon flown with three crew at a weight of 1,104 lb (501 kg). The temperatures are shown in Fig. 3.1 (see also the loading chart graph in Appendix 6).

The graph reveals some interesting facts. For lightly-loaded balloons the temperature actually decreases with height for quite a long way until it curves round and begins to increase. For balloons with a normal load the temperature increases all the way up.

If the air is warmer than ISA then, of course, the balloon temperature must be hotter at all altitudes. The increase in balloon temperature is more than the increase in air temperature. The 20° increase results in the balloon temperature rising about 30° at the surface and over 60° at altitude.

There are many other complications, particularly as the real atmosphere differs every day from the ISA standard. (See Chapter 6 for further discussion of this.)

For serious record attempts it is important to be thoroughly familiar with this theory, but for lesser flights it is enough to bear in mind the general effect, and keep an eye on the temperature gauge, being ready to slow or stop

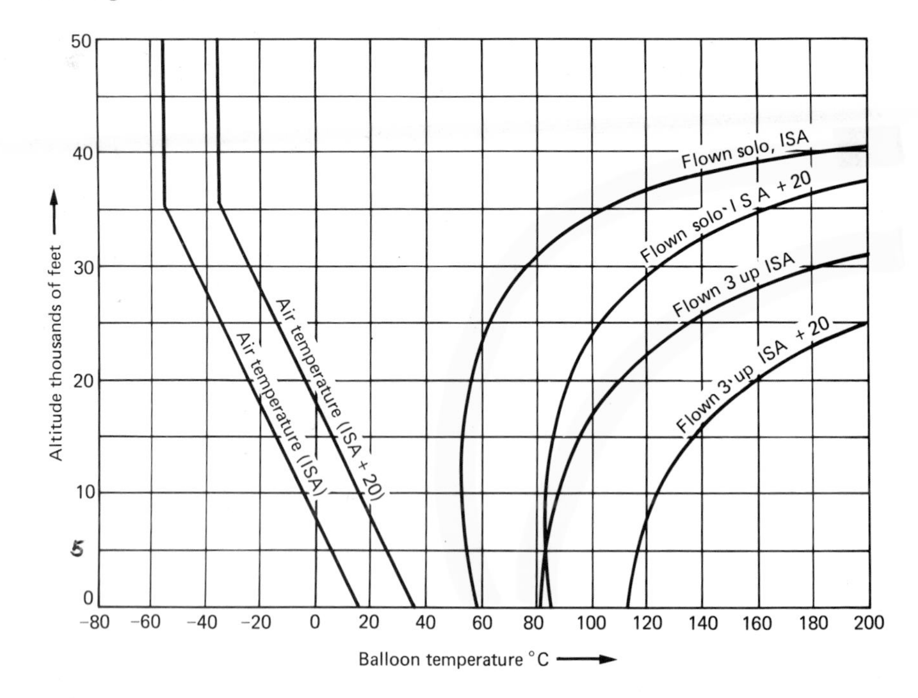

Fig. 3.1 Temperature of a 77,000 cu. ft balloon.

the climb as it approaches the 'red line'. Alternatively it is possible to use an ambient thermometer and loading chart.

Burner problems

As altitude increases, air density falls and this has an effect on the main balloon burner and pilot burner. The effect is likely to vary from one make of balloon to another, as burners are developed and tested for flight at low altitudes.

Typical experience seems to be that burners will perform without much difficulty up to 20,000 ft and above this will show a longer flame and slower combustion due to the shortage of oxygen. Above 35,000 ft, where the air pressure has fallen to less than one quarter of the surface level, a specially-designed burner is required.

Vapour pilot burners begin to give problems over 20,000 ft. Experiments have been made with oxygen assistance and several designs have been successful. One of the simplest I have seen was used by Sue Hazlett in capturing the women's world altitude record at 28,500 ft. She used a standard oxy-propane welder's torch – an 'off-the-shelf' burner for the mixed gases.

Oxygen

The requirement for oxygen varies greatly between individuals. Any balloonist contemplating flight at high altitudes should try to obtain training in a pressure chamber.

Training in a pressure chamber at 25,000 ft. Note the trainee's disconnected oxygen tube.

A typical exercise in the chamber at 25,000 ft pressure is to be asked to write one's name repeatedly on a sheet of paper after removing the oxygen mask. It goes well for the first twenty times or so, and then the subject starts to mis-spell occasionally and over the next few lines things go completely wrong. The spelling goes wild, the writing enlarges in size and finally deteriorates into incomprehensible scribbles. At this point the instructor will ask how the subject feels he is doing, and he will often reply, 'Fine, I don't feel any effect yet.' He is then invited to put his mask back on, but can't quite manage it and has to be helped. Full capacities return quite quickly when oxygen is restored and the subject is then astonished to see how his writing deteriorated.

The value of this training is to prove to the individual the danger of oxygen starvation and how impossible it is to keep a check on oneself.

The ability to withstand oxygen starvation depends on fitness and acclimatization. Climbers on Everest have exerted themselves over many hours near the summit (29,000 ft) without oxygen after weeks of acclimatization on the lower slopes, whereas any normally fit person taken from sea level to that height would be unconscious in a few minutes and would probably not survive. Fliers do not have the benefit of acclimatization, however, and a guide is as follows:

Height (ft)	*Oxygen requirements*
0–10,000	Oxygen not normally required. Exertion may cause shortness of breath and night vision may be impaired.
10,000–18,000	Oxygen should be used. Consciousness rarely lost in this range, but judgement is progressively impaired.
18,000–25,000	Oxygen is required to maintain judgement and consciousness.
25,000–40,000	Oxygen systems of proven reliability are required as an interruption of supply could result in brain damage or death.
Above 40,000	100% oxygen is no longer enough for normal breathing – some kind of pressure system is required.

Decompression sickness

A further hazard for high-altitude pilots is decompression sickness (also known as 'the bends') caused by nitrogen coming out of solution and forming bubbles in the body tissues. Symptoms are unusual under 30,000 ft and can be prevented by pre-breathing 100 per cent oxygen for some hours before the flight to 'wash out' the dissolved nitrogen.

Cold

The table of the ISA (see page 43) shows the temperature at height. Warm clothing is necessary, even for summer high flights.

Flight path

On high-altitude record flights the planned flight path is usually a fairly rapid climb continued until the envelope temperature reaches its limit, followed by a slower rate of climb until the fuel has dropped to the landing reserve. A cold descent is then carried out using the fuel reserve to round out and land.

On exploratory flights which are not record attempts safety can be improved by using a slightly less hectic flight profile and keeping a greater fuel reserve.

Parachutes

On any record flight, and on other flights above 10,000 ft it is wise to carry parachutes. On higher flights, above 25,000 ft, a more sophisticated type of parachute is required, including a portable oxygen supply and a barometric opening mechanism.

Air Traffic Control

Before flying high it is important to check on the requirements of Air Traffic

Control. Much balloon flying takes place under airways with bases at about 6,000 ft so it is important to review these before embarking on a high flight. There is never any excuse for wandering into an airway.

Above certain heights, flight level 245 (about 24,500 ft) in the UK, there are different rules and these include the need to carry radio and a transponder, unless an exemption has been obtained.

The reporter from the *Daily Telegraph* said it would be interesting to have pictures taken above the clouds and the Met. Office had confirmed that it was a layer of stratus, base about 3,000 ft, and 600 ft thick. I began to climb towards it.

At 3,000 ft the cloud still looked as far above as it had on the ground, so I continued climbing. We finally reached the base at 6,000 ft. It is a curious psychological effect, but a pilot who normally does most of his flying at 1,000 ft feels out of place and insecure at 6,000 ft – a totally irrational feeling, of course, because life depends on the security of the balloon at anything over 30 ft.

We entered the cloud and climbed uneventfully until we broke into the glorious sunshine at 7,000 ft. Flying at 200 ft over the cloud tops the feeling of security returned, equally irrationally. The scene was beautiful – to hover with no speed, enjoying sunshine which no earthbound mortals would see that day, gave a sense of privilege.

After a time we decided to go down, and found that the rate of descent decreased as we entered the cloud tops. Then it stopped altogether although I had not been burning. We were floating on the cloud surface like a cork on water. For quite a few seconds we stayed there until the balloon cooled enough to sink into the cloud.

As the balloon sank through the thick fog of the cloud something happened which gave me a chill of, this time, completely rational fear. I heard the sound of an aeroplane engine. I felt panic. We had no parachutes. The sound got louder. Why, I wondered, had I ever taken up this ballooning business? Feeling the need to do something I pulled on the vent line to speed our descent, and of course it made very little difference.

At last the sound reached its maximum, and began to recede. We all breathed again. The statistical chance of a collision outside controlled airspace is remote, and the aircraft probably was never closer to us than a mile but it was a nasty moment. We broke cloud at 6,000 ft and did not go back into it that day.

Distance and Duration Flying

The Fédération Aeronautique Internationale recognizes three classes of records: altitude, distance and duration (see Appendix 8). Altitude flying has been discussed in the preceding section, and distance and duration will be taken together, for they present the same kinds of problems.

Sporting balloon flights normally last for one to two hours. It is a good length of time and fits nicely into the social context of the sport, but it is easy to fly longer and farther. By taking fewer people and more tanks a flight of four or five hours is no great problem. When we try to push to the limits, however, several difficulties arise, some of which are considered below.

Fuel consumption

On a medium-sized balloon, a 43 lb (10 US gallon) tank will last, generally, for 45 minutes. When the balloon is more heavily loaded, it must be hotter to remain in flight, the cooling rate is greater and more fuel is consumed. All-up-weight is the dominant factor affecting fuel consumption but other variations come from a diverse range of causes:

Balloon size: At a given loading per unit volume large balloons are more efficient than small ones, as their volume per unit of surface area is greater.
Porosity: As balloons age, porosity increases,and with it, fuel consumption.
Solar gain: Some heat is picked up from the sun, and this effect is greater on darker coloured balloons. Fuel consumption is higher at night for any balloon, compared even with a cloudy day.
Climbing and descending: Expansion and contraction causes a pumping action which wafts out some warm air.
Turbulence: Causes a relative wind which cools the envelope, distorts it, forcing out some warm air, and deflects the heat of the flame.
Air temperature: Fuel economy is better in cold weather.

A scientific analysis of heat losses had been attempted, but is complicated. The heat losses are made up of several parts – the net loss due to radiation, the loss through conduction and convection and the loss through porosity and other leaks. All three of these components follow a different mathematical formula making precise prediction difficult. An approximate formula is to assume that the rate of cooling is proportional to the difference in temperature between the balloon and the ambient air.

The simple theory is a reasonably good predictor of fuel consumption although it has a slight error because the radiation part of the loss is proportional to the fourth power of the absolute temperature. This leads to the actual fuel consumption being slightly less than theory when the balloon is light, and more than theory when it is heavy.

The formula for fuel consumption rate is:

$$\text{Fuel Consumption} = CV^{2/3}\left[\frac{1}{1-\frac{W}{0{\cdot}07657V}} - 1\right] \text{ lb/min}$$

Where: W = all-up-weight (lb), V = balloon volume (cu. ft), C = the cooling coefficient, to be found experimentally for each balloon (in the example shown here it has a value of 0·00216).

(*Note:* the number 0·07657 is the air density, lb/cu. ft)

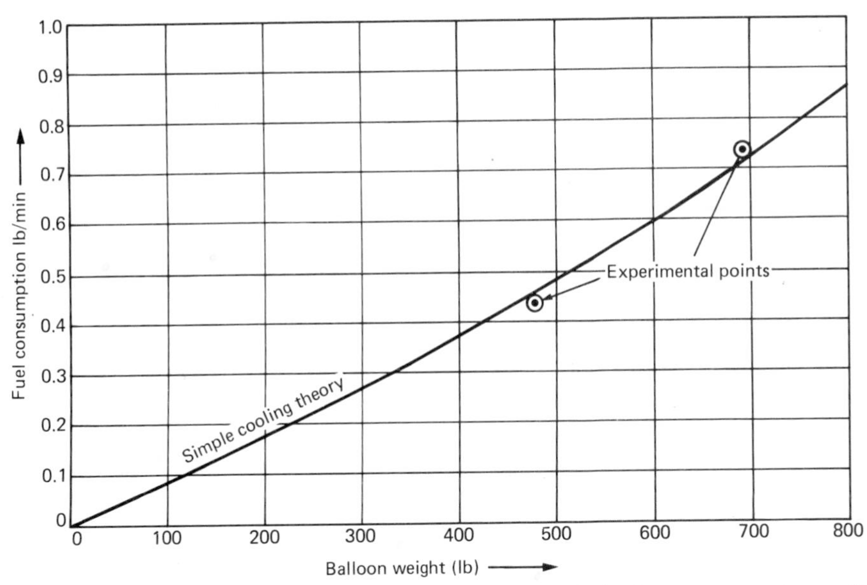

Fig. 3.2 Fuel consumption of a 42,000 cu. ft balloon.

Fig. 3.2 shows the experimentally-measured fuel consumption of a 42,000 cu. ft balloon together with the simple cooling theory curve.

The opposite formula assumes standard atmosphere sea level conditions, and heat loss proportional to envelope surface area and temperature difference.

Obviously the balloonist does not have to understand all of this for normal flying, but for record flights it is well worth measuring the cooling coefficient for the balloon which is to be used and calculating a programme of fuel usage.

Tank dropping

No world class distance or duration record could be achieved now without dropping empty fuel cylinders. The saving in fuel consumption which comes from the reduction in surplus weight is an essential advantage.

It is an expensive business to lose or damage the aluminium flight cylinders and some record flights have been made using the cheaper but heavier ordinary commercial steel cylinders early in the flight and dumping them as soon as possible. The extra weight is not so important if it is carried only for a short time.

The safety aspect of tank dropping is important. Over land it is illegal in the UK to drop anything except water or finely divided sand, and special permission must be obtained. It is not safe to drop from a great height, and it is best to descend low over the middle of a large field, when the crew is in sight, before dropping. Over the sea it is much easier to drop tanks safely, and a good look is enough to ensure that the area is totally clear.

Tank dropping should never be contemplated except for a serious record attempt. It is a drastic remedy and should be used sparingly.

Flight planning

When a record flight of over ten hours is contemplated, flight planning becomes a problem. A normal one-hour flight will cover 10 to 20 miles (15 to 30 km) and so in normal conditions a distance of up to 200 miles (300 km) is likely. It is difficult to cover this kind of distance in Europe, and impossible in the UK without a very good chance of meeting an obstacle such as controlled airspace, mountains or the sea. For a serious and exceptional record attempt permission can perhaps be obtained to pass through controlled airspace, although this will require prior arrangement and the use of a radio in flight.

The sea, if it is well situated, need not be a disadvantage. It imposes a need for safety equipment (see page 55) but also gives a dumping area for empty tanks. Both of the current (1980) records for distance and duration in class AX15 involved a channel crossing from England to France.

Timing is also important. Balloons have a better duration performance in winter, and at that time of year daylight is short. Recent long flights have been planned with a night take-off and landing near last light on the following day.

There are no fixed rules for planning long distance record flights except that they must be well considered in advance. Each time a record is pushed farther it is an original step into an area which no balloonist has experienced before.

Weather forecasting

A long flight needs weather which will remain good for 10 to 20 hours. It is a rare event in the UK, and even rarer that it can be forecast with confidence.

The weather forecasting problem is a little unusual. The balloon after taking off is, in a sense, part of the weather and should move along with it, with no rapid change in conditions and going wherever it goes. The problem then is to forecast the trajectory.

It is not completely true that the balloon lies stationary in a moving block of unchanging weather. The layers of the atmosphere are sliding over one another and at low altitude, where the balloon must fly at maximum weight at the beginning of the flight, the weather will be passing overhead just as it would be to a ground observer.

The gradual modifications which occur in an air mass will also happen on the day of the flight. After a take-off in the dark the pilot may observe the sequence of the day's weather. Early-morning mist may form and be cleared by the sun's heat. Further heating may generate convection covering the sky in cumulus clouds, and the balloonist can fly safely above these provided they are not developing at too great an altitude. As the sun's heat declines, ground cooling will cut off the thermals and, with luck, form a stable slow frictional layer for a safe landing.

The speed of the air mass will depend on the position of neighbouring pressure systems and the behaviour of the isobars. Converging isobars will cause a speed-up with dangerous conditions for landing, but diverging isobars imply that a parcel of air travelling along them will slow down.

Forecasting the behaviour of the pressure patterns and where the balloon will be situated in them twenty hours or so ahead is not easy, and the commitment not to land during dark or thermally hours or over the sea causes an unavoidable element of risk in long distance flying.

Record Breaking Formalities

To enjoy the honour of holding a record you must not only achieve it, but prove that you have achieved it to your national aero club, and, for world records, to the Fédération Aéronautique Internationale (FAI) in Paris. The proof can involve almost as much preparation work as the flight itself. It is always a shame if a record is achieved but cannot be made official because it cannot be proved. Some of the requirements of the sporting code can be criticized, but the need for careful scrutiny is quite real. A few years ago a gliding altitude record was awarded wrongly and the fraud was discovered only when the same man tried to claim a higher record, but was found out the second time. Such people make life difficult for the majority of honest sporting pilots.

Before attempting a record, a copy of the Sporting Code should be obtained from the FAI (for address see Appendix 10) and the rules for national records obtained from the national aero club. It is also necessary to hold an FAI sporting licence. This is usually granted to anyone who holds a Private Pilot's Licence from their own country.

A *steward* must be involved in any record attempt. He will be someone of trusted integrity, who is thoroughly experienced in balloon operations and regulations governing record homologation, and will be appointed by the national aero club. The steward is responsible for preparing the documentary proof for submission to the national aero club, and must satisfy himself that all the evidence required by the Sporting Code is present.

An *official observer* is appointed by the steward. The steward himself will be present at the ascent, but may not see the entire flight himself. He may delegate some of his responsibilities for collecting information to another responsible person.

A *barograph*, which functions like an altimeter but records altitude on a piece of smoked metal foil, is the principal instrument used to record altitude flights but is also used on distance and duration flights as proof that the balloon has not touched down. Barograph instruments must be sealed shut to make sure that a false trace is not put in, and sealed to the aircraft to prevent someone producing the trace in a pressure chamber. After the flight the barograph must be re-calibrated, and the calibration chart submitted among the documents.

If everything is satisfactory, and the dossier is accepted by the national aero club and the FAI, the pilot receives (for world records) a 'Diplôme de Record', a beautiful document, as a souvenir of his or her achievement.

Night Flying

A well-known American balloonist was once heard to say after a night flight that the really good thing about flying at night is that it makes you appreciate how good it is to have daylight to fly in. I do not believe that he really meant it, for the reason that balloonists make night flights, despite the considerable effort involved, is that the rewards make it worthwhile.

It is difficult to describe the fascination of night flying, just as it is difficult to put into words the beauty of lighter-than-air flight itself. The various parts have to be experienced to be appreciated – the lift-off into a black sky, friends at the headlight-illuminated launchpoint receding below, map reading by patterns of lights, the first glow of light in the east followed by sunrise, landing in the early morning calm – the most perfect part of the day – and the celebration breakfast.

Night flying is not particularly difficult, and need not present any problems to the average pilot, although some instruction is needed. The present British regulation for a licence not restricted to day flying is to have made at least two flights with a pilot qualified to fly at night, and this is about right.

Before flying at night several extra preparations must be made, and some suggestions for these are set out in the following paragraphs.

Pre-flight planning

A night flight needs more careful planning than normal for one reason only. As no sound technique for landing a balloon safely at night has yet been found, the pilot is committed, once airborne, not to land until there is enough daylight to see obstructions, including wires, clearly.

This imposes a need to think ahead. The time of the flight must be decided and strictly adhered to. Too early and it will be a longer wait than expected until daylight, too late and it will not be a night flight at all.

The balloon and its equipment will have been made ready on the preceding evening, and the preparations on the morning of the flight include:

1 Obtain a weather briefing from a 24-hour Met. Office. In particular, obtain wind speed and direction at 2,000 ft and on the surface, and the likely extent of formation of ground fogs.
2 Study the air map carefully for obstructions likely to be encountered on or near the downwind track. A decision will have to be made as to whether the flight is feasible or not.
3 If any controlled or special-rules airspace lies near the downwind track, telephone the appropriate Air Traffic Control Unit and explain the proposed flight and the difficulty of landing even if the balloon should diverge from the forecast track. Obtain their reactions. Often these will be favourable as there is usually very little traffic at this time of day. One must not, of course, plan to fly in controlled airspace, although the controller may be empowered to give permission for special-rules airspace. Again a decision must be made as to whether the flight is feasible or not.

Philip Clark taking off at night for his world distance record flight from Bristol to the Champagne area of France, 25 January 1978.

Equipment
Apart from a balloon in first-class condition, the following equipment should be prepared:
Navigation Light: A single red light suspended between five and ten metres below the basket of a strength of 'at least five Candela' showing in all directions is the legal requirement in the UK. In the USA a flashing red light and a steady white light are required.
Instruments: An altimeter is essential and a variometer and compass are useful.
Radio: Is not essential if all likely Air Traffic Control Units have been covered by prior telephone arrangements, but it is helpful if available.
Maps and handlamps: Must be provided.
Fuel: Must be adequate to last beyond sunrise with a good margin in reserve. Consumption is higher at night as there is no gain from the sun's heat.

Preparation and take-off
Preparing the balloon in the light of car headlights presents no unusual problems, except that it is easy to lose equipment. Once inflated, take-off is entirely normal – straight up into the inky blackness.

Flight
Once airborne, on moonless nights, the impression is of an utter blackness. Apart from the lit circle of the take-off point and the headlights of the retrieve car as it sets off, the countryside looks completely black. So much so, that it is impossible to estimate height, and one must find ground clearance from altimeter and map. Navigation is very easy from the patterns of lights in towns and villages.

It is important to stay high, at least 2,000 ft above ground level, to ensure clearance. Also animals possibly find a balloon at night more frightening than by day, so this is another reason for maintaining a good height.

Map reading is not difficult, but one effect which we call 'the trick of the lights' has been noticed on several flights. This is when a balloon travelling on a straight track appears to be changing course by as much as 180°. It is a purely visual effect and is always false when checked against the track drawn on the map.

On moonlit nights the outlines of fields and hedgerows can be seen, but it is still too dark to see the real danger – wires.

When daylight comes it is a very gradual process. First the merest glimmer in the east, so little that you are not sure if it is there or not, gradually increasing to full daylight, and then the most beautiful moment of all – sunrise. After this by descending to a lower altitude it is sometimes possible to watch the sun rise again!

Landing
The landing is a normal day landing, generally in ideal weather conditions.

However, fog is a common problem at the surface at this time of day. I have encountered this on two occasions but have managed to find suitable gaps through which to land, aided by the very low speed conditions.

Night landings

Although landings in darkness were commonplace 100 years ago on gas balloon flights, the only proven method of landing a balloon in the modern countryside laced with electric wires is to wait for daylight.

However, there are hopes of overcoming this. On a recent visit to the USA, together with the American pilot, Steve Langjahr, I completed what I believe is the first deliberate and safe landing of a hot-air balloon at night. We were using a duplicated halogen spotlight system designed by Bruce Comstock, and aided by a half moon and very slow conditions we decided to try a landing approach. It proved so easy to search out the field and its neighbours for wires, crops and animals that we decided to carry on and complete the landing.

It will take a lot more cautious experimentation on morning flights before we know whether this technique can be made reliable, but if so it will be rather fun to go flying on a winter evening, and land before the pubs shut, instead of the very unsocial hours which are involved at present.

Flying Over Water

For flights over water the central problem is weather forecasting – being sure that the wind and weather conditions will remain favourable until the balloon makes a landfall. The precautions cover what will happen if it does not.

Many balloonists do not appreciate the danger of being immersed in the sea. The danger of drowning can be averted with a good lifejacket, but the great killer is cold. Unconsciousness and death arrive in quick succession in low temperatures as Fig. 3.3 shows:

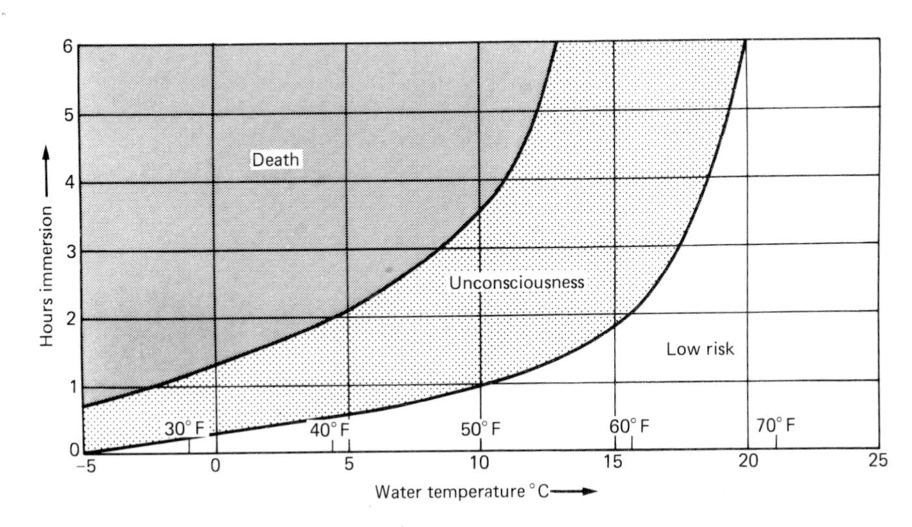

Fig. 3.3 Survival time in water: ordinary clothes.

FACING PAGE:
The Cameron D-96 powered hot-air airship.

Balloon flights, let's be realistic, always have a fair chance of not reaching a planned destination and it is madness to risk an immersion in water under 20 °C on the strength of a weather forecast.

An immersion-suit of the Beaufort type is ideal. Its waterproof construction and thin, stretched rubber neck and wrist seals allow clothes to remain dry and give almost complete protection. When temperatures are not so severe, a diver's wet suit is an adequate precaution.

A chase boat is a great advantage, but the difficulties of having the boat in the right place at the right time should not be underestimated, especially if the boatman is not familiar with balloons. Many years ago a lady pilot taking part in a race from an island to the mainland of California lost her life through putting trust in a boat which did not, in fact, turn up.

If the worst happens and a landing must be made in the water, the balloon is not necessarily lost. With slow and careful work it can be recovered. Metal parts should be washed as soon as possible with fresh water, as rapid corrosion will occur, but as far as is known salt water does no harm to balloon fabric.

When rescuing a balloon with a boat it is vital that the propeller be stopped, otherwise expensive damage to the envelope can be caused.

Mountain Flying

Mountain flying is one of the most exhilarating visual experiences possible in any sport. To be suspended in a basket of willow and cane above mighty snow-covered peaks, lower than an aeroplane but higher and without the effort of mountaineering, is to feel a wonderful sense of privilege.

Every year at Mürren in the Lauterbrunnen Valley in Switzerland gas balloonists gather for the annual High Alpine Ballooning week. There, directed by the octogenarian balloonist, Fred Dolder, they take off for adventures in that magical icing-sugar world.

Hot-air balloons are flown less often in the Alps, but hot-air meets have taken place in Austria, and hot-air balloonists have been attempting pioneering flights over mountains throughout the world.

It is not all beauty, however; there are also dangers to be faced. Mountain winds and weather make a flying environment which is very difficult for the hot-air balloonist. The wind-flow passing over the mountains creates rising currents on the windward slopes and turbulent down-currents on the lee slopes. This pattern is modified by strong thermal (or anabatic) flows up sun-heated mountain sides and drainage (or katabatic) flows on cooling slopes in the evening.

There is a school of thought which favours riding in all these complicated low-level currents and using skill and knowledge to avoid the areas of intense turbulence. Jo Starkbaum of Austria has achieved some wonderful flights and is the leading exponent of mountain flying. But there have been accidents too, and there can be no doubt that this must be ranked as a dangerous sport.

For Don with tha
'LENGAI'
9.3.74

ABOVE: Jo Starkbaum, the world's leading mountain balloonist, flying in his native Austria.

OPPOSITE: Alan and Joan Root flying over Mount Kilimanjaro.

At 17 knots and at about 3,500 ft we were treated to a fantastic view of Scafell and Great Gable, with a couple of climbers festooning the cliffs. It all seemed so effortless somehow to have floated up here from the deer park at Holker Hall whereas those poor earthbound mortals had slogged three or four hours of hard climbing to get half the view we were witnessing. David kindly located Wast Water with the only road for 20 miles and he pointed out the impossible landing country around us, all scree and cliff.

I was getting rather boastful about the flying side of it all and began accepting bets that I couldn't fly over the trig. point on Great Gable, when our cheekiness was suddenly and abruptly punished. I would describe the sensation as being picked up by the lapels by an eight foot giant and vigorously shaken, David claimed it was a ten foot giant, but I can assure you at that moment the difference was academic. The balloon was anything but the gently floating aerial platform that our manufacturers tell us they sell, and became a violent, distorted nightmare, In about twenty knots crosswind, a canopy can assume all sorts of horrible shapes and they become instantly many times worse when there is 3,000 ft of air below you! The top of the balloon was rapidly squashed down to the mid-line and we were nearly boiled alive by the belch of hot air expelled down into the basket. The whole thing then slipped sideways and we fell about a thousand feet towards the valley. It was at this point that I wondered if any of those mere mortal climbers would care to exchange positions with a nearly not mortal balloonist.

I suppose that our performance of aerobatics lasted about five minutes during which time we were steadily approaching the vertical faces of Great Gable in a game of aerial hopscotch. To complete the exercise we suddenly hit a strong updraught coming off the face which took us up to 6,000 ft and into cloud. We could almost hear the climbers calling for an encore but our joint decision was against it. In those five minutes we had used half a cylinder of fuel and even without David's calculations it was obvious that we could have difficulties getting out of the hills.

John Gore

During my own attempt with Mark Yarry to make the first crossing of a major Alpine range in 1972 we took the more cautious approach. We took off from Zermatt and climbed to more than 18,000 ft, passing over the Matterhorn and the Monte Rosa with 3,000 ft to spare. We encountered no significant turbulence and made our landing on flat ground in Italy.

When a landing must be made in a valley, it can sometimes be very difficult. Valley bottoms are usually littered with roads, railways, houses and power wires. When aiming for a valley landing, a steep, or even fully cold, descent may be desirable to get down to the valley bottom without being displaced too far from the aiming point. After rounding out there will only be a short time to find a safe landing field before the balloon is swept away again from the valley bottom. Sun-heated slopes will tend to pull the balloon into their thermal surface flows and back up towards the crests.

Mountain flying is difficult, but done with care and good planning it can be reasonably safe. Some advice:

1 Fly with a powerful, preferably double, burner unit.
2 Land with a generous fuel reserve.
3 Make the balloon as proof against turbulence as possible.
4 If a Velcro rip is used it should be protected with rip locks and the burner should be protected with a scoop or skirt.

Competition Ballooning

It is impossible to 'race' balloons in the literal sense because balloons cannot be steered and do not have any speed of their own; their speed is that of the air in which they are immersed. Nevertheless, hot-air ballooning now has vigorous competitive events with hard-fought national competitions, and the winners of these fight it out in the World Championships held every two years.

The traditional competition for gas balloons is the 'Foxhunt'. One balloon (the Fox) takes off, and after a time interval is followed by all the others. By moving up and down, and searching for different winds at different heights they try to follow the Fox and the winner is the balloon which lands closest to it.

Modern hot-air ballooning has adopted the 'Foxhunt', or 'Hare and Hounds' as it is often now called, and has added several other types of task. Most of the tasks require the dropping of a marker which consists of a bag of sand sewn onto a nylon streamer.

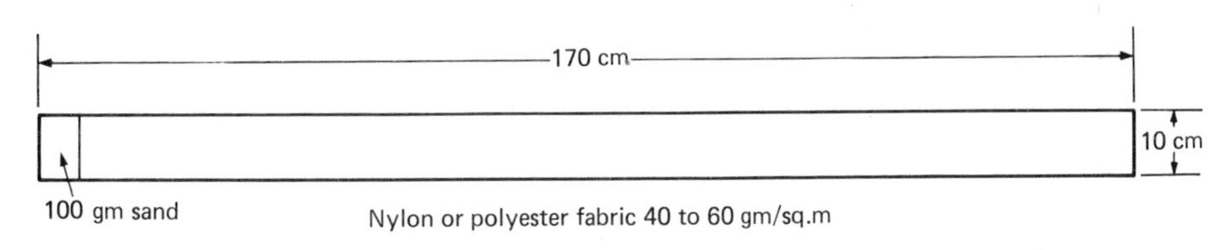

Fig. 3.4 Standard competition marker.

Skill in navigating balloons and dropping markers on the target has developed to such a degree that it is quite normal in a competition flight of twenty kilometres to find that the best two or three markers are within one metre of the target.

Some of the new tasks are:

Judge-declared goal: The competitors are given a goal somewhere downwind, and must try to drop their markers on it. It will usually be marked with a large white cross.

Pilot-declared goal: A similar task, except that the pilot declares his own goal by writing it on a slip of paper and handing it in before take-off.

Hesitation waltz: A curious name for a task which is really a judge-declared goal with a choice of several goals. The pilot can choose which one after take-off.
Fly-in: The balloons and crews go out from the contest field by a certain minimum distance, usually five kilometres and choose their own take-off point to fly back from. They take off in a field (after asking the landowner's permission) and fly back to drop their marker on the home field. This task has its drawbacks but is great spectator sport.
Elbow: The pilot is given two markers. After a certain minimum distance he drops the first, then after a further minimum distance, the second. The score is the greatest change of course between the two legs of the flight, measured in degrees.

An international convention of rules has been drawn up and scoring is taken very seriously indeed. Volunteer observers, usually balloon pilots or student pilots, fly as passengers, or follow on the ground, and measure marker drops on the map grid (see Chapter 5) with the greatest possible accuracy. A panel of judges computes the score, and at major events a jury is appointed to consider any protests.

For a student pilot, an invitation to act as observer in a major competition is well worth accepting for it gives an opportunity to observe the techniques of the top-class pilots at first hand.

Commercial Ballooning

In recent years many companies have come to appreciate the value of balloons as an advertisement. A balloon is made bearing the name and colours of the advertiser and is flown at shows and public events with the object of being seen by as many people as possible, both directly and through press and television. Occasionally shows and carnivals hire balloons which do not carry advertising to provide a display.

Show flying has many more difficulties than sport flying. The show is usually at the most turbulent and windy time of day – mid-afternoon – and the date is fixed far in advance. Every show pilot has often to contend with the situation of marginal weather and a disappointed show organizer. To be a good commercial pilot it is important to know when to say 'no', but also it requires experience and determination to get best results possible for the client. It is hard work and the easy-going atmosphere of sporting ballooning is in some ways a poor training ground.

A few years ago at a large agricultural show there were four commercial balloons hoping to fly from the arena. At the appointed time the wind was gusting to over twenty knots and it was quite impossible to put on a display. The show organizers intimated that there would be no more arena time available that day and three out of the four gave up and retired to the beer tent. Towards the end of the afternoon the wind dropped, and the fourth balloon took off from a car park upwind of the show ground and floated over

FACING PAGE:
Coca-Cola, an advertising balloon based in Hong Kong.

Coca-Cola
TRADE MARK REGD
G-B

in full view of the crowd and television cameras. Good commercial ballooning means trying harder.

Most countries require a more advanced qualification than the Private Pilot's Licence to do 'aerial work', as commercial flying is called in legal terms. In the USA there is a commercial licence. In the UK the authorities have been reluctant to issue commercial licences, although the law makes provision for it, and have issued 'exemptions' permitting aerial work by PPL holders.

Launching Hang Gliders

Dropping hang gliders from hot-air balloons has now been done by many pilots in several countries and, as far as I know, without incident. In fact, as a ballooning operation carried out in good weather conditions it is in no way difficult, and should be well within the scope of the average pilot.

I have dropped hang gliders on four occasions – three normal gliders and one two-seater – and this section aims to summarize this experience and note the main precautions involved.

Suspension

The weight of the glider should be taken by two adjacent shackles on the burner load frame. My suspension has always been a length of 4,000 lb balloon load tape knotted in a loop around the shackles and tied to the attachment at the top of the glider king post. It should be long enough to allow the balloon to be inflated on the ground alongside the hang glider.

The ability of the glider king post to withstand lifting is the responsibility of the hang glider pilot who should check this with his manufacturer.

Release mechanism

Many systems have been proposed, some rather complicated. Purpose-made mechanisms should be avoided as these tend to need development, and it is lucky if they work first time. My own system has been to cut the nylon tape with a knife at the balloon basket.

The cutting method is extremely simple and reliable, and the length of tape which remains streaming from the glider king post has no noticeable effect on its flying qualities. Important precautions are to stand back at the moment of release to avoid injury if the taut nylon springs back, and to make sure that a spare knife is available in the basket.

It is better, in my view, that the release should be under the control of the balloon pilot, and not the glider pilot, as an incorrect release, after the first fifty feet or so would be more dangerous to the balloon than to the glider.

FACING PAGE: The author taking off in a 77,000 cu. ft balloon lifting a two-seater hang glider.

Take-off

To carry out a smooth take-off the weather must be close to ideal from the balloonist's point of view. The load-carrying ability of the balloon for the ambient temperature should be checked on the loading chart.

The balloon, once inflated, should be allowed to lift off slowly, and be gently controlled by the suspension tape for as long as possible. Helpers should apply plenty of weight to the hang glider pilot to prevent a premature lift-off. It is very important to avoid jerking the hang glider off the ground as the extra load on the balloon would simply make it descend again, probably into the downwind obstacles. Instead a hands-on, hands-off routine should be tried, with helpers holding the hang glider pilot's shoulders.

It is the balloonist's responsibility to ensure a clean climb out as the glider is very vulnerable to any collision with obstacles. Once over 100 ft or so the glider is safe, even if released, and attention can be given to the climb.

Climb

During the climb the glider pilot cannot see the balloon, but he can hear everything the balloon pilot says. It is good, therefore, to keep him informed of progress. I generally call out the instrument readings for altitude and rate of climb at approximately 250 ft intervals. A climb rate of about five knots (500 ft/min, 2½ m/sec) seems satisfactory.

Release

It is important that the balloon slows its rate of climb and actually descends before releasing the weight of the glider, otherwise a dangerously fast rate of climb could occur. This is particularly important for Velcro rip balloons not fitted with safety locks. I have always waited for a descent of five knots before releasing. With the standard hang glider this declines to two knots descent after release, but after releasing the heavy two-seater it changed to four knots climb despite prolonged venting.

The Rogallo type glider launches beautifully. After a momentary vertical fall the nose dips and it slips forward into normal flight with the support tape streaming like a pennant from the king post.

Parachutes

I have always used parachutes, both on the balloon and glider pilots, and it is probably good to do this until experience is gained with this relatively new technique. In the long term, however, they should not be necessary.

The law

There is some doubt on the legal position of hang glider launching. In the UK permission must be sought on an 'each time' basis if anything or any person is to be dropped from an aircraft. If a glider were to be 'towed', however, rather than dropped, no formalities would be necessary.

Unfortunately, the Civil Aviation Authority (CAA) does not accept the latter interpretation, and is asking for an application on an 'each time' basis. It is to be hoped that a way of avoiding this can eventually be found as it wastes time both for the balloonist and the CAA and it is difficult to see its purpose.

4 Hot-Air Balloon Technology

It is not necessary to know how a car works to be a good driver, but it certainly helps. A detailed understanding of the balloon and its component parts enables a pilot to take care of his balloon, to handle emergencies better and to do simple maintenance avoiding the expense of a trip to the factory.

Envelopes

Materials and construction

Modern hot-air balloon envelopes are all of man-made fibres, mostly nylon, but a few polyester. With either fibre, a light and strong envelope can be constructed. Nylon is the stronger fibre by about 20 per cent weight for weight, and has the ability to stretch under load, which reduces its liability to damage. Polyester has a higher permitted operating temperature, but deteriorates more rapidly in conditions of heat and moisture.

Woven fabric, as it comes from the loom, is far too porous to make a practical balloon and it must be treated to seal the gaps between the fibres. The two main methods are coating, typically with a polyurethane varnish, and calendering, which is a heat-setting process where the fabric is compressed between hot rollers.

No fabric is perfect. The life of a hot-air balloon envelope is usually 400 flying hours depending on how it is treated. Ultra-violet light, heat, and repeated folding combine to cause degradation. As a balloon ages porosity will increase fuel consumption, and tests made on annual inspection will reveal a loss of fabric strength. Fortunately, deterioration does not have much effect on safety. Fabrics are generally more than one hundred times as strong as they need to be to sustain flight loads, and weakness begins to show itself with minor damage during ground handling long before it presents a flight risk. Porosity can be a risk, as it makes the balloon more difficult to fly, but it is also very obvious to the pilot.

Webbing tapes are used in balloon construction to provide strength and their performance is quite astonishing. A one-inch (25 mm) tubular nylon tape has a typical break strength of 4,000 lb (1,800 kg). Balloons may have twelve or more of these tapes, and yet more than twice the weight of the basket could be supported by one tape.

Nomex fabric is used in the part of the envelope closest to the burner flame. Its use is limited because of its high cost but its fire-resistant qualities make it very desirable around the base where burn damage during inflation was common in early balloons.

Various stitch and seam types are used in balloon construction. The two main stitch types are shown in Fig. 4.1.

Fig. 4.1 *Above:* Lockstitch. *Below:* Chainstitch.

The lockstitch is the stronger and neater system and is made by the traditional sewing machine using two threads, one in the needle and one in a bobbin under the machine bed. The chainstitch is made from a single thread, and in some versions can be unravelled by pulling at one end. It also presents a heavy appearance with its double or sometimes triple threads on the reverse side. Its advantage is cheapness as production can go ahead unhindered by bobbin changing.

Seams also come in two main types as shown in Fig. 4.2.

Fig. 4.2 *Above:* French felled seam. *Below:* Simple overlap seam.

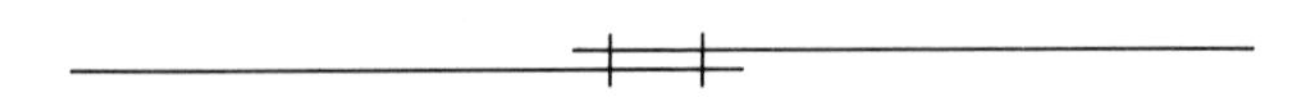

The French felled seam is the higher quality but more expensive seam. The simple overlap version is cheaper but is not so strong, lacks protection for the raw fabric edges and, used over a whole balloon, adds to air permeability.

Sailmakers and hang glider manufacturers use the flat seam universally, but their job is different. They wish to present a smooth surface to an aerodynamic flow whereas the balloon designer wants to contain pressure.

Design

A typical balloon is shown in Fig. 4.3. The main suspension loads are passed from the stainless steel rigging wires to the vertical load tapes via a carefully tested sewn joint. The vertical tapes are uninterrupted right up to the crown of the balloon where they pass over the top aperture to unite with strong sewn joints to a metal crown ring.

Air pressure is contained by the bulbous gores. A high degree of curvature leads to a low skin tension in any pressure vessel, and this principle makes the bulbous gore the most efficient form of construction. Other designs can be quite satisfactory, however, and may be the best choice for aesthetic reasons. The natural-shape balloon, by using a carefully calculated mathematical shape, has zero horizontal stress and the vertical stress can be carried by closely-spaced vertical tapes. Beware of balloon designs which boast of a tight smooth skin. This is easy to achieve by tailoring the balloon shape to increase skin stress, but sacrifices resistance to damage for a small aesthetic advantage.

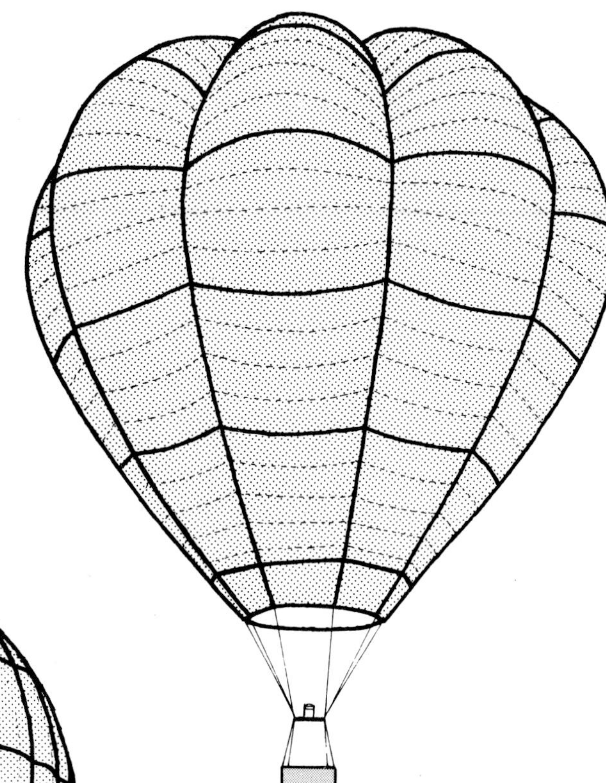

Fig. 4.3 O-type balloon.

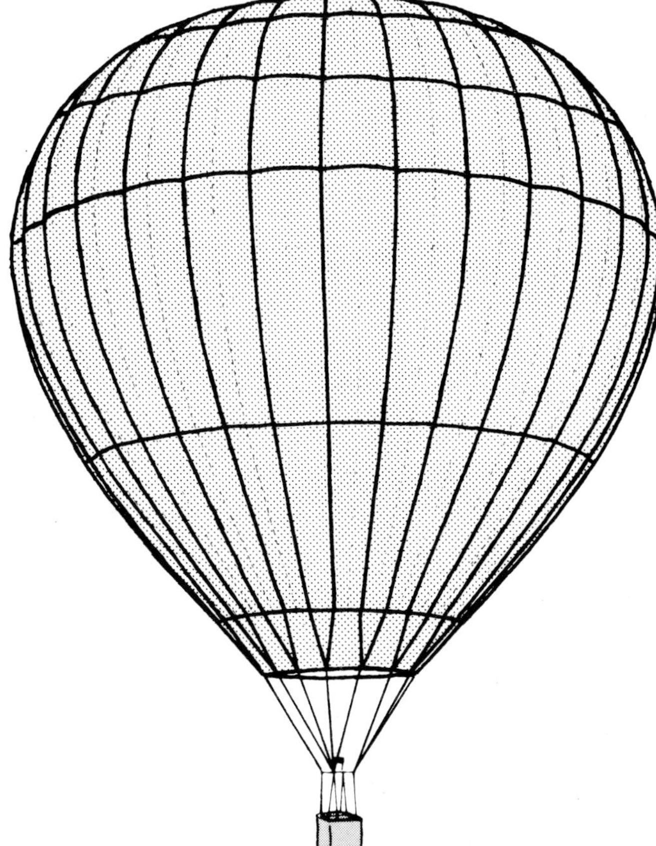

Fig. 4.4 N-type balloon.

An example of a 'natural shape' balloon. A Cameron N-77 advertising a stadium in Wales.

Horizontal load tapes are very important. In normal flight they bear no load at all, but they act as powerful rip stoppers. They give an assurance that any damage would be unable to spread enough to produce a catastrophic deflation.

Around the base, most balloons nowadays incorporate a ring of Nomex panels. These give resistance to burn damage which cuts down on repair bills. The base of the vertical load tapes should also be protected from burn damage, for obvious reasons, and ideally the protector should still allow ready inspection of the tape attachment points.

What is the natural shape?

Frequently balloon designers refer to the 'natural shape' balloon. Strictly speaking there is no such thing as a natural balloon – they are all artificial – but one mathematical procedure generates a shape which is both efficient and beautiful. It should perhaps more appropriately be called the 'zero horizontal stress balloon'.

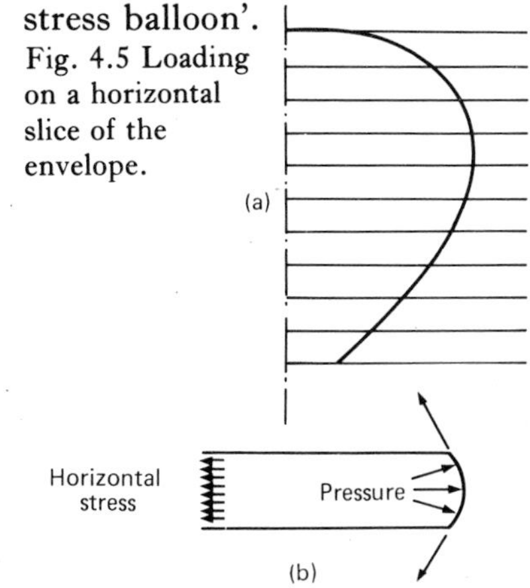

Fig. 4.5 Loading on a horizontal slice of the envelope.

When a balloon designer calculates the stresses on an envelope he considers it one slice at a time.

By taking the lift in each slice and the angle of the surface at each cutting plane, it is simple to work out the vertical tension in the fabric at each level.

Then, by considering each slice on its own the horizontal forces are calculated. The horizontal components of the vertical fabric stress help to contain the pressure, but any left-over pressure force must be contained by horizontal fabric tension.

The more curved the balloon shape, the more the vertical tensions will contain the pressure, and the lower the horizontal stress. This is why tall, thin balloons have a high horizontal stress whereas fatter balloons have a low horizontal stress.

If a very short and fat balloon were constructed it would give a negative horizontal tension – a compression – which fabric cannot support. The balloon would change shape to give zero horizontal stress with vertical wrinkling in the fabric.

When the balloon is designed for zero horizontal stress a particularly elegant shape results. The vertical force per gore is also a constant amount. When a balloon is designed with closely-spaced vertical load tapes it is possible to have a smooth balloon with little stress in the fabric.

The 'natural shape' balloon has the following characteristics:

1. Zero horizontal stress.
2. Closely-spaced vertical tapes which carry a constant load over their whole length.

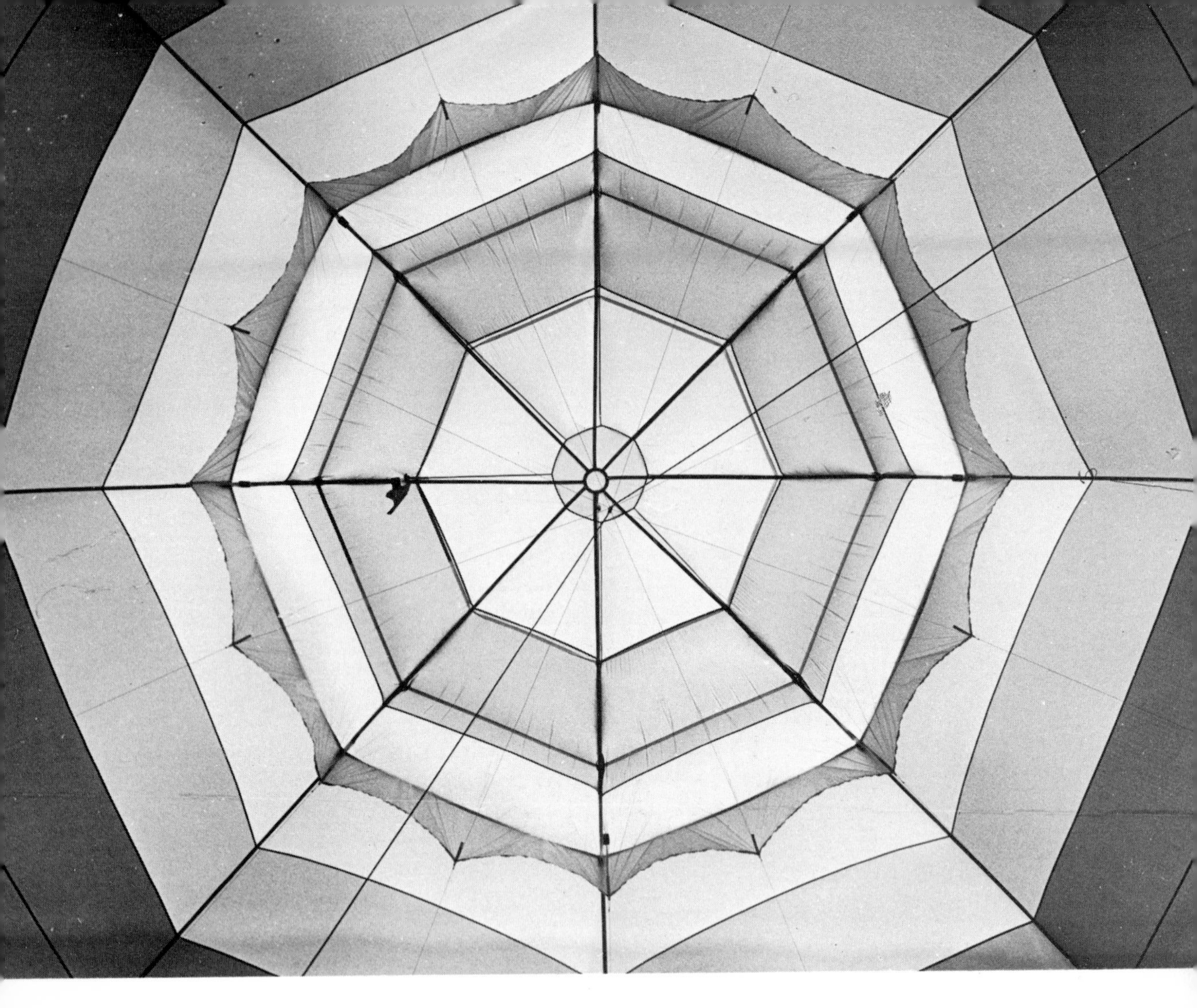

Parachute vent system. Note how the parachute bulges through the aperture forming a tight seal against the taut top edge of the balloon.

3 A very low vertical fabric stress, where the cut of the panels allows this to be efficiently transferred to the vertical tapes.

There is no simple mathematical equation for the curved shape of the natural balloon, but by using a computer and calculating the loads on many very fine slices the shape can be found with great accuracy.

Examples of balloons built to the natural shape are Raven and Cameron 'N' types.

Parachute valve systems

The control system shown above is the parachute top (see also Fig. 2.1). The hole in the top of the balloon is closed by a simple parachute-shaped device. A pulley at the base of the shroud lines can be pulled down by the red operating line from the basket. The parachute is returned by air pressure and is maintained centrally over the aperture by centralizing lines attached either to the load tapes or to more resilient points in the centre of the bulbous gores.

With a parachute top a good seal is important and several manufacturers offer proprietary designs which claim advantages in achieving this. The dominant factor, however, is adjustment of the centralizing lines. If these are too long the parachute edge will come close to the aperture and show gaps; if too short, gaps will be produced by the parachute being held down, off the aperture. Adjustment is seldom required and it is important only that the pilot can recognize *when* it is required.

Velcro rip panels

In recent years the parachute top has been increasing in popularity at the expense of the other main type, the Velcro rip panel. Velcro, a ribbon of tiny nylon hooks which cling tightly when pressed into a mating ribbon of fluffy loops, provides a useful sealing material. Rip panels may be circular, as shown, or may be made up of a 'pie slice' of two or three vertical gores. A red line from the basket is used to pull out the panel.

Velcro circular rip: Sequence of operation.

Rip panels have given good service since modern hot-air ballooning started, although a series of accidents a few years ago, including the only fatal accident in Britain, prompted an increase in safety precautions. On circular panels the vertical load tapes pass freely over the panel to the crown ring. Strict rules have been laid down to ensure that these tapes are shorter than the corresponding dimension on the panel to ensure that the load is carried by the tapes with no part of it passing through the Velcro joint. Rip locks – a series of locks which hold the Velcro seal at several points until the rip line is pulled – have been adopted by most manufacturers.

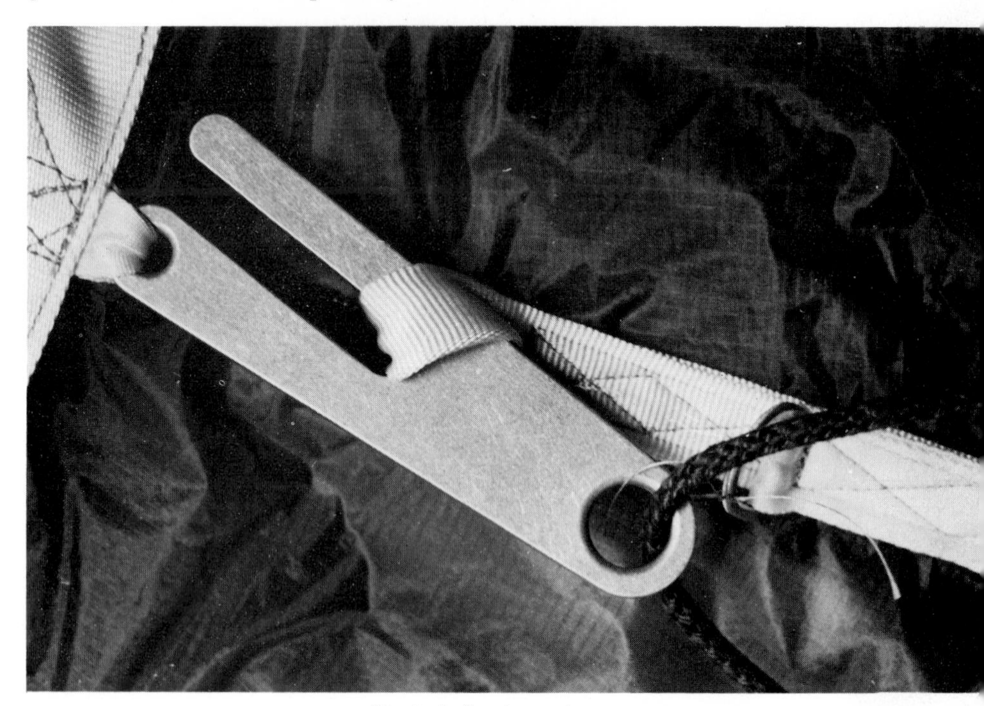

Rip lock (hook type).

When a Velcro rip is used, it is only used on the final landing, as it cannot be resealed for continued flight. An additional means of allowing a controlled release of hot air is necessary and this is provided by the side vent. A window frame made of load tape is installed in the side of the balloon and is covered by a blind of fabric. A line from the bottom of the blind passes up above the window, around a pulley and down to the basket. A pull on this line opens the valve and a piece of elastic recloses it when the line is released (see illustration).

I am often asked which is the better system, and there is no direct answer. Currently I prefer the parachute for smaller balloons as it is so much more convenient in use. The twenty-minute ritual of 'doing up the rip panel' is dispensed with. Parachutes, however, are designed smaller than rip panels

Envelope side vent viewed from the basket. *Left:* closed. *Right:* open.

because their size is limited by the physical strength of the pilot. For larger balloons the Velcro panel is the only viable system.

Skirts and scoops

Most balloons use a scoop or skirt around the base. The skirt is a tapering cylinder of fabric which shields the flame from side gusts. To maintain its shape the bottom edge is usually reinforced with a strip of spring steel. Skirts are useful in flight, but make inflation without a fan difficult and, because of the spring steel, are difficult to pack.

The scoop is a patented 'Cameron Balloons' feature, and it works by increasing the pressure inside the balloon. On the ground a balloon is affected by the wind blowing on the side trying to deflate it. The wind passing the open base actually makes matters worse by creating a low pressure which sucks the air out (Fig. 4.6a). When a scoop is fitted the wind at the base flows into the balloon, causing a pressure increase at all points on the envelope surface and helping to resist the force of the wind on the side (Fig. 4.6b).

The scoop gives a dramatic improvement when inflating on exposed sites and tethering. When airborne it gives a protection from gusts which is as good as a skirt despite its asymmetry, and it is easier to pack away, and cheaper.

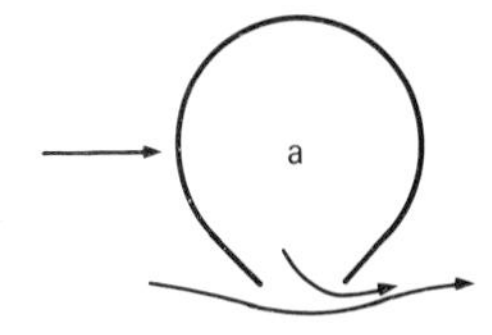

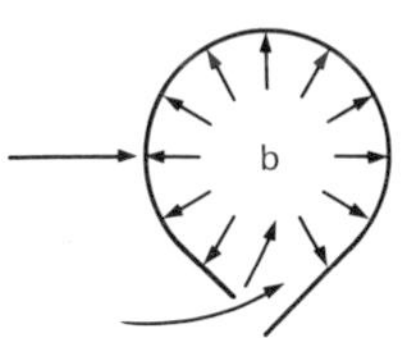

Fig. 4.6 Effect of scoop.

Burners and Fuel Systems

The propane burner is one of the cornerstones of the hot-air balloon revival. Other fuels have been tried but the convenience and controllability of propane are hard to equal.

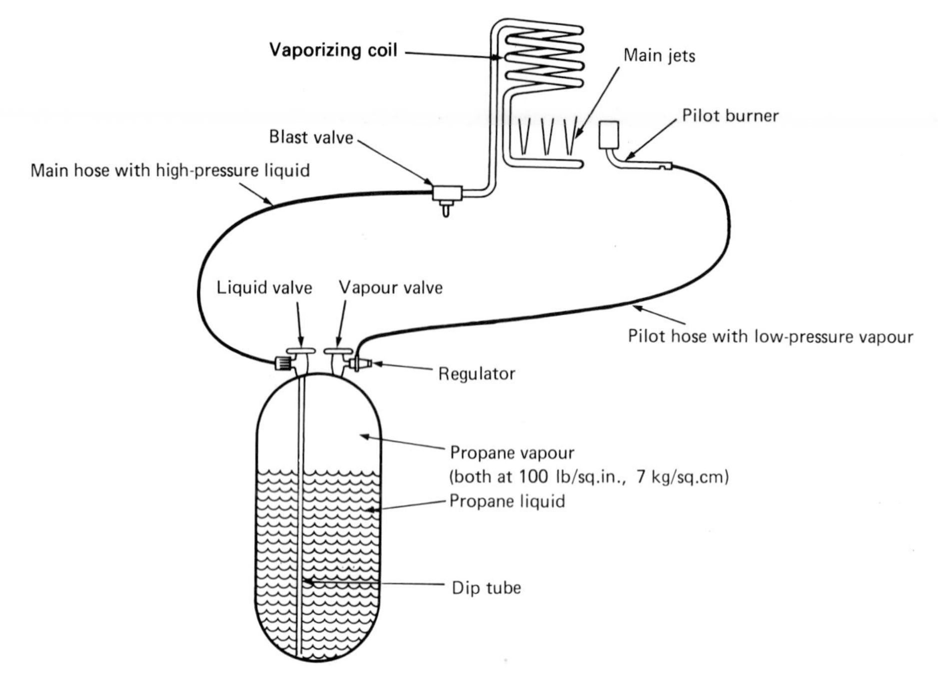

Fig. 4.7 Principle of hot-air balloon burner.

Fig. 4.7 shows the essential features of the propane burner which are common to every make of balloon.

Liquid propane is forced by its own vapour pressure up the dip tube and main hose to the blast valve where it is admitted to the vaporizing coil of the burner. It is turned into vapour by the heat of the flame and emerges from the jets where it mixes with air and burns. The liquid offtake is necessary, as vapour taken in such quantities from a tank would be replaced by boiling in the liquid, absorbing so much latent heat that the tank would quickly freeze and lose pressure.

The pilot system is completely separate and takes its supply from only one cylinder, the 'master'. As its consumption is very small, it is satisfactory to use a vapour offtake. This passes through a regulator which reduces its pressure to a low level suitable for the Bunsen-type pilot burner.

Fuel tanks

The type of fuel tank in most common use is the Worthington 10 US gallon (43 lb/19·5 kg) aluminium type produced in the USA. This is illustrated in Fig. 4.8, and it is surprising how much there is to learn about it.

The internal dip tube passes down from the liquid valve point and bends so that it ends immediately below the two small holes in the guard ring (not visible in Fig. 4.8 due to cut-away). This means that the tube will draw liquid when the tank is vertical, or when it is horizontal with the two holes down. It is designed this way so that the tank can be mounted by these two holes on a forklift truck, which requires a liquid feed.